I10638858

SYNTHESIS
and ORGANISATION
in the BACTERIAL CELL

C I B A LECTURES IN MICROBIAL BIOCHEMISTRY

SYNTHESIS
and ORGANISATION
in the BACTERIAL CELL

By E. F. GALE

1959

NEW YORK · JOHN WILEY & SONS, INC.
London · Chapman & Hall, Ltd.

Library
State College
Indiana, Penna.

C. 1

The CIBA Lectures in Microbial Biochemistry were established in 1955 at the Institute of Microbiology, Rutgers, the State University of New Jersey, through the support of CIBA Pharmaceutical Products Inc., Summit, N. J. The lectures are given in the spring of each year at the Institute of Microbiology, New Brunswick, N. J.

Copyright © 1959 by John Wiley & Sons, Inc.

All rights reserved
This book or any part thereof must not be reproduced in any form without the written permission of the publisher.

Library of Congress Catalog Card Number: 59-14985
Printed in the United States of America

Library
State College
Indiana, Penna.

589.95 G131
c. 1

PREFACE

The material in this book formed the basis of three lectures given at the Institute of Microbiology, Rutgers, the State University of New Jersey, on March 18–20, 1959. The theme is biosynthesis, with emphasis on the synthesis of proteins and nucleic acids. The biological formation of macromolecules is a subject which, after a long lag period, is now in a phase of exponential growth. My own experience has been exclusively with bacteria, and, consequently, the account presented here is mainly concerned with these organisms. We are far from sure that the mechanisms we study are the same in other tissues, and it is useful to try to correlate results obtained by different workers with different biological preparations; in this way we may hope to tell to what extent the biological organisation of the preparation is an essential part of the mechanism. No one can work with micro-organisms without wondering how they manage to do all they do, despite the rough treatment to which we—and Nature—subject them. We cannot unravel biochemical problems without study-

v

ing the nature of the cell, and the cell is a manifestation of dynamic biochemistry. The close connection between structural organisation and synthesis of macromolecules provides the reason for the title and the mode of presentation of the material in the following pages.

Lectures are restricted in time, and their preparation involves a considerable degree of selection of material. Publication of lectures is consequently a dubious business, as they cannot be as full as reviews should be, nor can the published account reasonably contain all the illustrations necessary for keeping an audience awake. Consequently the chapters that follow do not pretend to be comprehensive surveys of the subjects chosen. They contain a certain amount of detail and reference to the literature which it is not possible to present in lectures—even if references are added as subtitles to slides in the manner of the translation of foreign language films. A lecturer must choose his matter with a view to brevity, interest, and, perhaps, drama and can only hope that his readers, as opposed to his auditors, will regard omissions in this light rather than attribute them to ignorance, prejudice, or malice.

I am most grateful to CIBA Pharmaceutical Products Inc. and to Professor W. J. Nickerson for the invitation to give these lectures and for the opportunity to visit the Institute where so much outstanding microbiological research has been carried out. I wish also to acknowledge the incalculable debt I owe to the many people who have worked, as colleagues, collaborators, students, or visitors, in the Unit for Chemical Microbiology at Cambridge and whose experimental and dialectical skill have contributed much of the material presented in the following pages.

Medical Research Council Unit   E. F. GALE
  for Chemical Microbiology
Cambridge, England
September, 1959

CONTENTS

STRUCTURE AND ORGANISATION
IN THE BACTERIAL CELL

> Dear God, what marvels there be in so small
> a creature.
>
> **Leeuwenhoek's draughtsman**

The attention of biochemists has been attracted for many
years by bacteria, partly because they have such a high rate
of metabolic activity and partly because they display such
a wide range of chemical activity. Those of us whose task
it is to introduce students of biochemistry to the joys of
microbiology usually begin our lectures by discoursing on
the size of the bacterial cell and pointing out that, as an
organism decreases in size, so does the ratio of its surface
area to volume increase, and, as a result, the smaller the
creature, the greater must be its exergonic metabolism in
order to offset the greater loss of heat from its surface.
Somewhere here a reference to the differences in magnitude
among elephants, men, mice, and micro-organisms generally
creeps in, and the lesson is imparted that the bacterial cell
respires and reproduces at rates 100–1000 times as great as
those of Man. Then we discourse on the cell as a chemist,

referring to the synthesis of substances as complex as ribo-flavin and chlorophyll from carbon dioxide and gaseous nitrogen, and to the ability of bacteria to derive metabolic energy from substrates as diverse as paraffin hydrocarbons, phenols, and carbohydrates, or by the oxidation of such apparently unrewarding substances as sulphur or carbon monoxide. A mention of the ease and speed of growth of many bacteria leads to the moral that the most fascinating and expedient approach to biochemistry lies through micro-biology.

Almost 300 years ago, Leeuwenhoek made the first micro-scope which was sufficiently powerful to enable him to see and describe bacteria. His letters of that time reflect his great wonder that such small creatures could exist and live. Our sense of wonder is no less today; in fact, the greater scientific precision of our present knowledge has increased our curiosity concerning the nature of these smallest of free-living creatures. Comparative biochemical studies indi-cate that many fundamental metabolic systems are essen-tially similar in bacteria and higher creatures, but in bac-teria these systems are encompassed in a cell so much smaller than those which form higher organisms. An "av-erage" bacterial cell has dimensions of the order of $1-3$ μ and is smaller than the nucleus or even some of the mito-chondria of animal and plant cells. Does this mean that the bacterial cell is simpler in structure or organisation? If so, it is still a most competent living creature and should there-fore provide an excellent subject for investigation of the integration and organisation of biochemical and biophysi-cal events that give rise to life. The bacterium is certainly free from some of the complexities of multicellular or-ganisms with their intercellular fluids, complex buffering systems, and hormonal control. We believe that the Bernard aphorism, "La fixité du milieu intérieur est la condition de la vie libre," must apply to these creatures, so how does the "simple" bacterial cell exist so happily in environments of widely different physicochemical condition? That there are differences between bacterial and mammalian cells is shown by the existence of antibiotics that are toxic to the former but not to the latter. Does the selectivity of such drugs reside in their ability to combine with structures specific to the micro-organism or to inhibit metabolic processes peculiar to the parasite? These are some of the questions which occupy the modern microbiologist who has become blasé about mere matters of rates and complexities of chemical reactions. They are questions to which the research work of the last few years has begun to supply the beginnings of answers. And it is with some of these beginnings that I hope to deal in the course of these lectures.

The Structure of the Bacterial Cell

The use of the electron microscope, with a resolving power of 20 Å or less, together with the development of techniques for sectioning bacteria, has enabled us to learn something of the structure of the bacterial cell. The drastic treatment which a section has to undergo before an image is obtained on the screen of an electron microscope is such that a great deal of caution has to be exercised in interpretation of the results. Accomplished experts can now produce pictures such as those shown in Plate I. Inspection of the photographs reveals the presence of an outer layer or layers to the cell and a somewhat amorphous organisation within the cell. Two sorts of material can be distinguished inside the cell: transparent material in and around the "core" of the cell, corresponding in distribution with the chromatin demonstrated by cytologists, and outer, electron-dense substance that, on close examination, appears to consist of closely packed granules. In view of the uncertainties

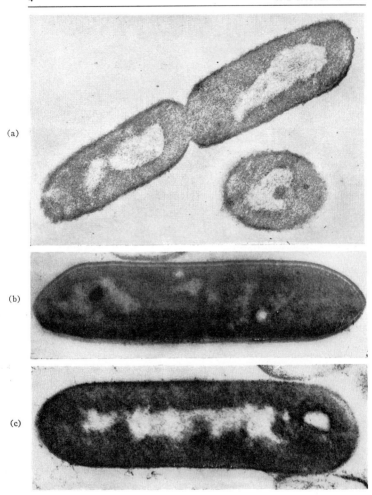

(a)

(b)

(c)

Plate I. Electron micrographs of longitudinal sections of some bacterial cells. (a) *Escherichia coli* (×35,000). By courtesy of Professor E. Kellenberger, Laboratoire de Biophysique, Geneva. (b and c) *Bacillus polymyxa* (×20,000). By courtesy of Professor P. E. Holbert, the Institute of Microbiology, Rutgers, the State University of New Jersey (*J. Biophys. Biochem: Cytol.*, to be published).

of interpretation, it is highly desirable to investigate the existence and nature of these structures by other means and, wherever possible, to isolate the various components for separate examination and analysis. Studies of this sort have been attended with considerable success during recent years, particularly those concerned with the surface structures of the cell. As a result, we can now speak of the existence of these structures with confidence and of their functions with credibility.

The Wall of the Bacterial Cell

The pioneer work of Dawson [1] first made the investigation of bacterial cell walls a possibility. He showed that shaking suspensions of bacteria with small glass beads in a sonic vibrator resulted in separation of walls from cells so that it was possible to isolate the wall fraction and study the walls in a clean condition. Walls from a wide variety of bacteria have now been separated and studied. In some cases, electron microscopy has revealed the presence of a delicate structure in the wall. Thus Houwink [2] has shown that the inner surface of the wall from a spirillum has the appearance of a mosaic of close-packed spheres, and Plate II shows the detailed structure of walls from *Bacillus megaterium* examined in freeze-dried preparations.[3]

The chemical composition of such wall preparations has been investigated by a number of workers.[4–6] Cummins and Harris [6] found marked differences in the composition of walls from different species and suggested that the composition could be used as a factor in classification. Walls contain lipid, polysaccharides, amino sugars, and amino acid complexes; major differences are found between walls from Gram-negative and Gram-positive bacteria in that the former have a higher lipid content (11–22% compared with 1–4% in Gram-positive preparations) and give a complete

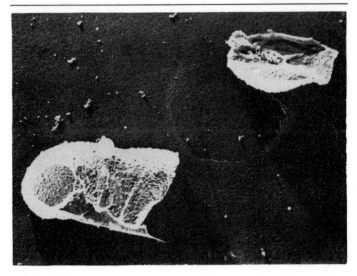

Plate II. Electron micrograph of walls of *Bacillus megaterium* (×20,000). By courtesy of Dr. M. R. J. Salton (ref. 3).

range of amino acids on hydrolysis, whereas the latter are devoid of aromatic amino acids and contain peptide-like complexes yielding, in some cases, as few as four amino acids only. The amino acids found in walls are unusual in that a high proportion of the glutamic acid and alanine is present as the D-isomer while diaminopimelic acid forms a component of many walls but is not present in the cytoplasmic proteins. Table 1 shows the components found in a number of wall preparations from Gram-positive bacteria, and it can be seen that they all possess glucosamine, muramic acid, alanine, glutamic acid, and either lysine or diaminopimelic acid. Quantitative analyses show that the ratio of muramic acid to D-glutamic acid is approximately 1 for a number of different wall preparations.[7]

Some eight years ago Park [8] showed that a new group of substances accumulates in staphylococci growing in the presence of penicillin. These substances were found to be complexes of amino acids and uridine 5'-pyrophosphate N-acetylmuramic acid with a formula tentatively assigned as in Fig. 1. As knowledge of the composition of cell walls developed, it became clear that the muramic acid and the amino acids found in peptide combination with it are

TABLE 1

Chemical Composition of Cell Walls Isolated from Some Gram-Positive Bacteria [6]

	S. pyogenes (A)	S. pyogenes (B)	S. faecalis	C. diphtheriae	C. pyogenes	S. aureus	S. lutea	A. viridans	M. cinnabareus	L. casei	L. plantarum
Arabinose	−	−	−	+	−	−	−	−	+	..	−
Rhamnose	+	+	+	−	+	−	−	−	−	+	−
Galactose	−	+	+	+	−	−	−	−	+	+	−
Glucose	−	−	+	−	+	−	+	+	−	+	+
Mannose	−	−	+	+	..	−	−	−	..	+	+
Glucosamine	+	+	+	+	+	+	+	+	+	+	+
Galactosamine	−	−	+	−	+	−	−	+	+	+	−
Muramic acid	+	+	+	+	+	+	+	+	+	+	+
Aspartic acid	..	..	..	..	..	..	..	..	..	+	−
Alanine	+	+	+	+	+	+	+	+	+	+	+
Glutamic acid	+	+	+	+	+	+	+	+	+	+	+
Lysine	+	+	+	..	+	+	+	+	..	+	..
Diaminopimelic acid	..	..	..	+	..	..	..	..	+	..	+
Serine	..	..	..	..	..	..	..	..	..	..	..
Glycine	..	..	..	..	..	+	+	..	..	..	..

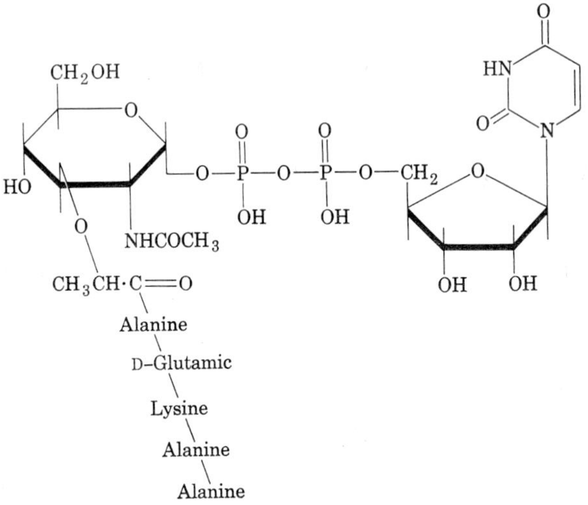

Fig. 1.

components of the staphylococcal wall and that the relative proportions of the amino acids and muramic acid are the same in the wall and in the nucleotide accumulating in the penicillin-treated cell. This has led to the suggestion [9] that the muramic acid peptide is probably part of the cell wall structure. A further component, accounting for the phosphorus of the wall preparation, has recently been described by Baddiley and his colleagues,[10] who have shown the presence of polymers of ribitol phosphate in the walls of *Staphylococcus aureus, Lactobacillus arabinosus,* and *Bacillus subtilis.* The polyribitol complexes contain other substances and have been named the "teichoic acids." Teichoic acids isolated from *L. arabinosus* and *B. subtilis* contain α-glucosyl residues joined to ribitol and O-alanyl groups probably linked to the glucose; the teichoic acid isolated from a strain of *S. aureus* contains N-acyl glucosamine in place of glucose. Figure 2 gives a representation of the teichoic acid structure which forms 40–60% of the wall of the three organisms so far investigated.

The walls of certain organisms can be rendered soluble

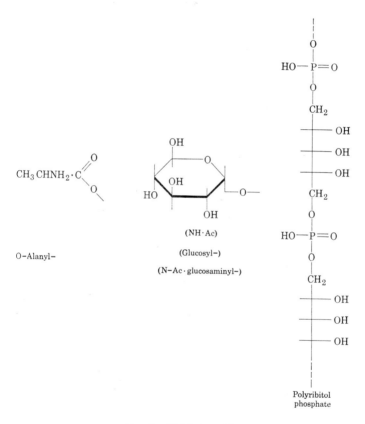

(NH·Ac)

O–Alanyl–

(Glucosyl–)

(N–Ac·glucosaminyl–)

Polyribitol
phosphate

Fig. 2.   Teichoic acids.

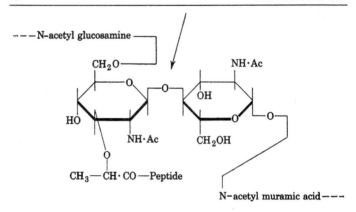

Fig. 3. Postulated structure attacked by lysozyme.[11]

by digestion with lysozyme. Brumfitt, Wardlaw, and Park [11] have proposed that this enzyme hydrolyses β 1–4 links between N-acetylmuramic acid and N-acetylglucosamine and that lysozyme-sensitive walls contain repeating units of these two sugars linked as in Fig. 3. The walls of *Micrococcus lysodeikticus* and *B. megaterium* fall into this category, and suspensions of these walls are cleared by incubation with lysozyme. If suspensions of whole cells are incubated with the enzyme in dilute buffer solution, lysis takes place but, if the osmotic pressure of the suspending medium is raised by the addition of sucrose to a concentration of 0.1–0.2M, the walls dissolve to leave naked protoplasts (Weibull [12]). The protoplasts are highly sensitive to osmotic shock and undergo immediate lysis if the medium is diluted with water. Whole cells are not lysed by suspension in water; the preparation of "washed suspensions" is a common technique used by microbiologists for studying the biochemical activities of bacteria. The difference in osmotic sensitivity between whole cells and protoplasts lies in the properties

of the walls which protect the protoplasts in much the same
way that the outer casing protects the inner tube of the
car tyre.   Mitchell and Moyle [13] have measured the osmotic
pressure within bacterial cells and found that it may be
of the order of 20–25 atmospheres for Gram-positive cocci
and 5–6 atmospheres for Gram-negative rods.

Anything which impairs the structure of the wall will
render the cell osmotically sensitive.   In the case of *B. megaterium* the wall can be removed by digestion with lysozyme,
and a number of other treatments are now known which
will result in the formation of osmotically sensitive protoplasts or spheroplasts (in which the wall substance may be
damaged but not necessarily absent [14]).   Diaminopimelic acid
is a component of the wall but not of the cell protein, so
that limitation of this amino acid could lead to restriction
of wall synthesis without effect on protein synthesis, and
Meadow, Hoare, and Work [15] found that growth of organisms requiring diaminopimelic acid in the presence of
limited amounts of that amino acid results in eventual lysis
during which the intermediate formation of spherical forms
can be observed.[16]   It has been mentioned above that growth
of staphylococci in the presence of penicillin leads to the
accumulation of uridine nucleotides combined with muramic acid and peptides of the same composition as those
found in staphylococcal walls; this finding led Park and
Strominger [9] to suggest that penicillin interferes with the
synthesis of cell walls and that the nucleotide complexes
which then accumulate may be precursors of cell wall substance.   Buchanan and co-workers [17] have also observed the
accumulation of cytidine diphosphate ribitol in penicillin-
treated staphylococci, and this may arise, again, from the
action of penicillin in interfering with wall synthesis and
teichoic acid formation.   If penicillin acts by disorganising
the formation of cell walls, then its bactericidal effect is

due to subsequent osmotic lysis of the spheroplast and it
should be possible to prevent the lysis by raising the osmotic
pressure of the medium. Ledeberg [18] found that *Escherichia
coli* produces osmotically sensitive spherical forms if it is
grown in the presence of penicillin, sucrose, and magnesium. On removal of the penicillin, a proportion of the
spherical forms gives rise to normal rod-shaped cells once
more. This observation has since been confirmed by other
workers,[19, 20] while Hancock [21] has demonstrated the formation of osmotically sensitive forms of *S. aureus* by growth
in the presence of penicillin and suitable concentrations of
stabilising substances such as sucrose, sodium chloride, glutamic acid, or ammonium chloride. Glycerol provides no
stabilisation, presumably since it is able to penetrate the
cell membranes.

Gale and Folkes [22] found that the effects of bacitracin
on staphylococci are essentially similar to those produced
by penicillin, while Paine [23] found that cells highly resistant
to penicillin are also resistant to bacitracin. Abraham [24] has
reported that bacitracin can induce the formation of "protoplasts" of cells growing in hypertonic media and also gives
rise to accumulation within the cells of uridine nucleotide
complexes similar to those found by Park in penicillin-
treated staphylococci. The substances giving rise to these
effects have now been extended to include oxamycin and
high concentrations of glycine.[25]

Incorporation of Amino Acids into Wall Substance. If
washed suspensions of staphylococci are incubated with glucose and a labelled amino acid, the amino acid becomes
incorporated into the trichloroacetic acid-precipitable fraction of the cells. In our early studies, we observed that the
nature of the incorporation process appeared to differ with
the conditions of incubation.[22] In particular, the time-
course of incorporation of an amino acid such as glutamic

acid was different when that amino acid was the only one added to the incubation medium (condition 1) from the time-course taking place when the labelled amino acid was one component in a mixture of the 18 amino acids necessary for protein synthesis (condition 2). Incorporation was found to be sensitive to certain antibiotics, but again the degree of inhibition obtained varied with the experimental conditions. Particularly puzzling was the finding that the incorporation of several amino acids, when studied under condition 1, was inhibited by these antibiotics to an extent which never reached 100% even at high concentrations but, instead, reached a plateau value which differed with the amino acid studied. Thus the incorporation of glutamic acid, glycine, alanine, and aspartic acid was inhibited by penicillin or bacitracin, but this inhibition amounted to less than 50% so that a considerable proportion of the incorporation was penicillin-resistant. Similarly, incorporation of these amino acids was partially inhibited by chloramphenicol, a proportion again being completely resistant. The degree of inhibition produced by penicillin was not the same as that produced by chloramphenicol, but the two antibiotics appeared to have complementary actions.

It is now known that glutamic acid, glycine, and alanine occur in the cell wall peptides of the staphylococcus and that such peptides are included in the trichloroacetic acid-precipitable fraction of the cells. Mandelstam and Rogers [26] and Hancock and Park,[27] working independently, have shown that incorporation of these amino acids can take place directly into the wall substance of staphylococci, that the process can occur in the absence of protein synthesis and is chloramphenicol-resistant but penicillin-sensitive. Table 2 shows the incorporation of glutamic acid that will take place into the wall and protein fractions of intact staphylococci when these are incubated with glucose and

TABLE 2

Incorporation of Glutamic Acid by Intact *Staphylococcus aureus*

Washed cells incubated in buffered saline at pH 6.5 in the presence of glucose and ^{14}C-labelled glutamic acid with other amino acids as shown below. Cells harvested after 60 min. at 37° and fractionated according to ref. 27.

Condition	Amino Acids Present	Glutamic Acid Incorporated, $m\mu$moles/60 min./mg. dry weight cells	
		Protein Fraction	Wall Fraction
1	Glutamic acid only	1.9	8.6
2	18 amino acids	55.1	12.4
3	Glutamic acid, glycine, lysine, alanine	0.2	13.4

glutamic acid alone (condition 1), the complete mixture of eighteen amino acids necessary for protein synthesis (condition 2), or the four amino acids of the wall peptide (condition 3). It can be seen that incorporation of glutamic acid under condition 3 takes place almost entirely into the wall fraction, whereas under condition 2 incorporation takes place into both wall and protein fractions. The nature of condition 1 incorporation will be discussed in a later section, but a high proportion of the incorporated radioactivity is clearly associated with the wall fraction in these experiments with intact cells. The results in Table 2 emphasise the independence of the processes leading to the formation of wall peptides on the one hand and proteins on the other.

Table 3 shows the degree of inhibition of the incorporation of glutamic acid, under various experimental conditions, by chloramphenicol and penicillin.   Penicillin is without inhibitory action on protein synthesis but markedly decreases incorporation into the wall fraction; chloramphenicol, on the other hand, is without significant action on incorporation into the wall fraction but strongly inhibits incorporation into the protein fraction of the cell.   From these various studies, it is clear that the incorporation of amino acids such as glutamic acid and glycine can involve at least two independent series of processes: those leading to the synthesis of proteins and those leading to the formation of cell walls.   Inhibitors such as chloramphenicol and penicillin which give a plateau type of inhibition presumably do not affect one of these series, whereas inhibitors such as aureomycin which bring about complete suppression of incorporation must affect both series.   Incubation of

TABLE 3

Inhibition by Antibiotics of Glutamic Acid Incorporation by *Staphylococcus aureus*

Conditions as for Table 2 in the presence and absence of 30 μg./ml. of either chloramphenicol or penicillin.

Condition	$\%$ Inhibition by Chloramphenicol of Incorporation into		$\%$ Inhibition by Penicillin of Incorporation into	
	Protein Fraction	Wall Fraction	Protein Fraction	Wall Fraction
1	58	0	0	91
2	94	0	0	78
3	—	7	—	91

staphylococci under condition 3 provides a method whereby the action of drugs on the incorporation of amino acids into the wall fraction can be studied, and in this way Park[28] has confirmed that penicillin, bacitracin, oxamycin, and high concentrations of glycine or aureomycin (chlortetracycline) interfere with the processes leading to cell wall formation. Aureomycin at bactericidal concentrations inhibits protein synthesis but is without effect on the incorporation of lysine into the wall fraction under condition 3.

The Cell Membrane

Removal of the cell wall from *Bacillus megaterium* leaves spherical protoplasts. If these are liberated in a hypotonic medium, lysis takes place and the protoplasts rupture, leaving 'ghosts" or broken membranes which can be separated from the lysate by high speed centrifugation. Analyses of membranes, or material derived therefrom, have been made for *Micrococcus lysodeikticus*,[29] *B. megaterium*,[30] and *Staphylococcus aureus*.[31] The composition of the membrane is very different from that of the cell wall, and the three groups of investigators agree that the membrane can be considered essentially lipoprotein in nature. The membrane contains true protein in that hydrolysis yields all the usual L-amino acids (but not diaminopimelic acid) found in proteins, while lipid accounts for 20–30% of the membrane but less than 1% of the wall in these Gram-positive species. Table 4 summarises the main differences between the two structures in *M. lysodeikticus*.[29] Nucleic acid appears to be absent from the membranes, but the cytochrome system is probably present and Mitchell and Moyle [31] report, as shown below, the presence of a number of enzymes in particles derived from staphylococcal membranes.

Early studies by Gale [32] and Taylor [33] showed that Gram-positive bacteria are able to concentrate certain amino

TABLE 4

Composition of the Cell Wall and Membrane from *Micrococcus lysodeikticus* [29]

	Cell Wall	Protoplast Membrane
Proportion of whole cell	20–25%	9–10%
Lipid content	Approx. 1%	28%
Amino acids	Alanine, glutamic acid, lysine, glycine	Probably all amino acids of protein as protein forms 50% of membrane
Carbohydrate	Glucose (10%)	Mannose (20%) and traces of other sugars
Amino sugars	20% glucosamine, muramic acid	2%

acids within the cell so that a concentration gradient of 300–400× may exist across the surface structures. Other workers have shown that phosphates, phosphate esters,[34] purines, pyrimidines,[35] and other soluble substances can exist in a highly concentrated state within the cells, and it is such substances that contribute to the high internal osmotic pressure of the bacterial cell. Concentration gradients of this order indicate the presence of osmotic barriers in the surface structures of the cell. Mitchell and Moyle [13] and Weibull [36] have investigated the permeability of intact cells and protoplasts derived therefrom and have found that the impermeable volume for glutamic acid or phosphate ions is approximately the volume of the protoplast, suggesting that the osmotic barrier lies in the protoplast membrane. The fact that the protoplast possesses all the metabolic and biosynthetic properties of the intact cell [37] emphasises that it is afforded the same protection from environmental variations as the intact cell.

Disorganisation of the Membrane. If the membrane acts as an osmotic barrier, it would follow that disorganisation of the membrane should result in leakage of the internal solutes from the cell. Hotchkiss [34] showed that treatment of staphylococci with tyrocidin or other surface-active substances resulted in release of soluble P- and N-containing substances from the cell, and Gale and Taylor [38] followed up this observation by showing that the action of these detergent substances brought about the release of free amino acids concentrated within intact cells. There is a direct relationship between the amount of tyrocidin or detergent added and the number of cells rendered non-viable and permeable. Electron microscope examination of cells treated in this way showed changes in the surface structures, but proof that the membrane is the site of action came from the studies of Newton [39-42] on the action of polymyxin. Polymyxin is a cyclic polypeptide which is particularly effective against Gram-negative bacteria. In growth-inhibitory concentrations it brings about the release of soluble constituents from sensitive cells. Newton synthesised a fluorescent derivative of polymyxin which retained its antibiotic properties and he was then able to demonstrate by fluorescence photomicrography that the derivative was fixed by the protoplast membrane (see Plate III). This provided a most elegant demonstration not only of the site of action of the antibiotic but also of the rôle of the membrane in conserving the internal medium of the cell.

The action of polymyxin is antagonised by cations, and Newton [40] investigated the comparative efficiency of a series of cations in competing with polymyxin for the bacterial membrane. The cations fell into a series similar to that displayed by their affinity for phospholipids, and it seems

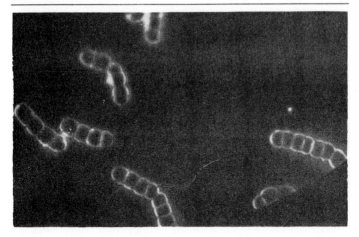

Plate III. Fluorescence photomicrograph of *Bacillus megaterium* after treatment with fluorescent polymyxin (×2000). By courtesy of Dr. B. A. Newton (University of Cambridge).

probable that the antibiotic produces its alteration in the properties of the membrane by reacting with phospholipid groups in the membrane. We now have a number of poly-peptide antibiotics which are surface-active and appear to act on bacteria by bringing about disorganisation of the membrane; tyrocidin, gramicidin S, circulin, and polymyxin belong to this group. Polymyxin possesses a methyloctanoic acid residue [43] which would confer lipophylic properties on the cyclic peptide, and the recent stereochemical studies of Schwyzer [44] indicate that gramicidin S exists in the form of an antiparallel pleated sheet with the lipophylic leucyl and valyl groups orientated on one side while the polar ornithyl residues emerge on the opposite side of the sheet. It there-fore seems possible that these antibiotics owe their peculiar properties to their possession of groups, or an orientation of groups, which enables them to combine with, or possibly penetrate, the lipoprotein of the cell membrane.

Enzymic Activities. The existence of protein in the membrane raises the question whether any of this protein is enzymically active. Mitchell and Moyle [31] have reported that the membrane of *Staphylococcus aureus* is unstable and readily breaks down into lipoprotein particles. They have studied the distribution of a number of enzymes between the membrane particles and the cytoplasm and find that some 90% of the succinic, lactic, malic, and formic dehydrogenases, acid phosphatase, and cytochrome system of the cell occurs in close association with the membrane particles. Weibull and Bergstrom [30] also report that the cytochrome system of *Bacillus megaterium* is located in the protoplast membrane.

Active Transport across the Membrane. The protoplast membrane is impermeable to many soluble metabolites. The ability of the bacterial cell to maintain that constancy of the internal medium that is essential to life rests on the properties of the membrane. Nevertheless some of the substances which are retained by the osmotic barrier are also essential nutrients. The staphylococcus, which maintains an internal concentration of glutamic acid far greater than that in the external environment, may be unable to synthesise that amino acid and must, consequently, be able to assimilate glutamic acid from the external medium. In this case we have an essential nutrient separated from the inside of the cell by an impermeable membrane. Gale [32] found that Gram-positive cocci are able to take up glutamic acid from the medium and concentrate the amino acid within the cell if that cell is supplied with a source of energy such as glucose. When exergonic metabolism takes place, glutamic acid passes into the cell by a process of active transport across the membrane.

Our knowledge of active transport in bacteria has recently been extended by the studies of Monod and his colleagues [45] on the utilisation of sugars by mutants of *Escherichia coli*. Lactose is utilised by *E. coli* after hydrolysis within the cells by β-galactosidase, and cells which cannot form the enzyme are unable to grow on lactose as carbon source. However, certain mutants of *E. coli* have been found which are unable to utilise lactose although they possess a normal complement of β-galactosidase and a normal mechanism for its formation. Investigation showed that these "cryptic" mutants are unable to utilise lactose because the sugar cannot penetrate the cell membrane to reach the site of action of the enzyme. In lactose-utilising mutants, a mechanism exists for the active transport of lactose across the membrane; this mechanism is distinct from β-galactosidase and its formation under independent genetic control. Examination of the conditions necessary for the formation of the transport mechanism revealed that (a) it was inducible, requiring the presence of galactosides, (b) it occurred only when protein synthesis took place, (c) it was prevented by inhibitors of protein synthesis, and (d) the mechanism when formed was specific for the transport of galactosides. The transport mechanism thus appears to involve a specific protein displaying specificity of action, and Monod has suggested that such a component can be regarded as an enzyme and has proposed the name "permease" for proteins of this nature.

The passage of amino acids into the staphylococcus can be attributed to such permeases. In the original studies of Gale [32] and Taylor,[33] only Gram-positive bacteria were found capable of concentrating free amino acids within the cell, but the technique used at that time involved extensive washing of the cells in water before the internal amino acids were estimated by an enzymic method. Cohen and

Rickenberg [46] have now shown that Gram-negative bacteria
can also effect high concentration gradients of amino acids
but that there is rapid equilibration between the internal
and external media; consequently, internal amino acids are
rapidly lost to the medium when Gram-negative cells are
washed in water. The difference between Gram-positive
and Gram-negative cells appears to lie, not in the ability to
concentrate amino acids, but in the ability to retain amino
acids within the cells when these are placed in water. There
is little or no outward diffusion of amino acids from the
staphylococcus but rapid equilibration with the external
medium in the case of *E. coli*. Cohen and Rickenberg [46]
found that valine, leucine, and isoleucine compete for the
permease which effects their passage into *E. coli;* as a result, valine concentrated within the cell can be "chased"
or displaced by leucine or isoleucine but not by methionine
or phenylalanine. The displacement is stereospecific as
L-valine is not displaced by D-leucine or D-isoleucine. Similarly methionine or phenylalanine can be concentrated
within the cells, but neither is displaced by valine although
phenylalanine can be displaced by L-*p*-fluorophenylalanine.
The authors suggest that amino acids are concentrated by
independent permeases, although the specificity may not be
restricted to one amino acid (as in the case of valine, leucine, and isoleucine).

The Membrane as a Site of Protein Synthesis. The protoplast is able to synthesise protein [37] and, since it is readily
lysed, offers an opportunity for investigation of the site of
protein synthesis in the bacterial cell. McQuillen [37] reported that preparations of membranes made under certain
conditions from protoplasts of *Bacillus megaterium* are able
to incorporate amino acids, and Spiegelman [47] obtained protein synthesis in osmotically shocked protoplasts. Butler,
Crathorn, and Hunter [48] followed the course of incorpora-

tion of amino acids into subcellular fractions of intact *B. megaterium* cells and found that the protoplast membrane fraction became labelled most rapidly, the cytoplasmic proteins acquiring label more slowly. Protoplast membrane preparations were able to incorporate amino acids into their proteins, and, when labelled membranes were incubated with unlabelled cytoplasm, some of the radioactivity was transferred to the cytoplasmic proteins. From these experiments the authors concluded that the initial stages of protein synthesis take place at sites on, or closely associated with, the protoplast membrane. Crathorn and Hunter [49] also found that ^{14}C-labelled alanine became incorporated into the protein of membrane fractions in the presence of chloramphenicol at a concentration which inhibited incorporation into cytoplasmic protein. From the variation with time of the amount of radioactivity in the membrane and wall fractions, it was suggested that the cell wall peptide is also first elaborated in the membrane. Beljanski and Ochoa [50] have obtained chloramphenicol-sensitive incorporation of amino acids into fragments of wall and membrane obtained from *Alcaligenes faecalis*. In recent studies, Spiegelman [51] has prepared spheroplasts from *Escherichia coli* by growth in the presence of penicillin and sucrose, disrupted their structure, and separated membrane fragments, ribonucleoprotein particles, and the soluble protein fraction. The ability to synthesise protein and ribonucleic acid was found to reside in the membrane fragments only. Connell, Lengyel, and Warner [52] have separated ribonucleoprotein particles and membrane fragments from Azotobacter and found that the bulk of the ability to incorporate amino acids lies in the fragment preparation, the activity of the particles being of a much lower order.

It would appear that there is considerable evidence pointing to a rôle of the protoplast membrane in protein synthesis although it is not clear, in many of the preparations cited above, to what extent the membrane preparations may be contaminated with cytoplasmic material. It is generally accepted today that nucleic acids are involved in protein synthesis, so that it is interesting to note that nucleic acid appears to be absent from the protoplast membrane [29, 30] although membrane fragments are, according to Spiegelman, able to synthesise ribonucleic acid. Should the membrane prove to be the site of protein synthesis, then the process must involve a relationship between the membrane and cytoplasmic materials in contact with it, and the existence of such a relationship might explain the frequent failures to obtain protein synthesis in "cell-free" preparations and separated fractions.

Penicillin and Membrane Activities. One of the earliest actions of penicillin on *Staphylococcus aureus* to be described was impairment of the ability of treated cells to concentrate free glutamic acid.[53] Penicillin has no action on the concentration of glutamic acid by non-growing cells, but, if the antibiotic is added to the growth medium, then the ability of the growing cells to concentrate the free amino acid is progressively impaired and abolished after a period of 70–90 min. The utilisation of the free amino acid in the "internal pool" of the cell is unaffected (i.e., protein synthesis is unaffected), so that the net result is a progressive fall in the concentration of free glutamic acid within the cell. The same type of effect has also been described for the accumulation within the cell of other amino acids [21, 54] but not for lysine which accumulates inside the staphylococcus by a passive distribution.[32] The active transport of amino acids such as glutamic acid into the cell is now attributed to permeases, and one explanation of these effects would be an inhibition by penicillin of permeases and their formation. It has been shown above that peni-

Library
State College
Indiana Penna.

589.95 G131
C./

cillin disorganises the synthesis of cell wall material, with the result that cells growing in its presence evolve as osmotically sensitive forms which eventually undergo lysis. The impairment of glutamic acid accumulation takes place long before any significant lysis of the cells can be observed,[53] and the question arises whether the loss of permease activity is a direct effect of penicillin or whether it arises as a secondary effect of the disorganisation of the membrane due to damage to the wall. The osmotically sensitive forms produced by growth in the presence of penicillin can be stabilised by the presence in the medium of high concentrations ($1-2M$) of non-penetrating solutes such as sucrose, sodium chloride, glutamic acid, and ammonium chloride.[21] The presence of such stabilising agents slows the growth to some extent, but Hancock[21] has now shown that, in their presence, penicillin has no effect on the ability of the cells to accumulate free amino acids such as glutamic acid or proline.

Penicillin has no inhibitory action on protein synthesis unless present in a concentration several orders higher than that required to inhibit growth or cell wall synthesis. However, the induced formation of β-galactosidase is inhibited by low concentrations of penicillin or bacitracin.[55, 56] Hancock[21] finds, again, that, although 1 unit of penicillin will give 90% inhibition of β-galactosidase formation in exponentially growing cells, this effect is prevented by the presence of stabilising agents in the medium. Glycerol has no stabilising effect. Table 5 summarises the actions of penicillin in the presence and absence of a stabilising concentration of sodium chloride, and it can be seen that the antibiotic has no effect on amino acid accumulation (permease) or β-galactosidase formation if the protoplast is stabilised; the impairment of cell wall synthesis is not abolished by the presence of stabilisers.

TABLE 5

Effects of Penicillin on the Properties of *Staphylococcus aureus* Growing in the Presence and Absence of Sodium Chloride as Stabiliser [21]

The organism is grown in two parallel cultures, one of which contains 1.2M NaCl added to the medium. Each culture is divided into two and 1 intern. unit penicillin/ml. added to one half; after incubation for 1 hr. at 37° all cultures are harvested and their properties examined. The results are expressed in each case as the % of the control culture without penicillin.

	1.2M NaCl	
	Absent	Present
Total free amino acids within cells	68	100
^{14}C-Glutamic acid uptake	8	100
^{14}C-Proline uptake	11	95
β-Galactosidase synthesis	6	100
^{14}C-Lysine incorporation into cell wall fraction (condition 3)	19	35
Increase in optical density at 700 mμ during 60 min.	26	25

The question arises: why should these processes be affected by penicillin in the absence of stabilising agents? Penicillin gives rise to the accumulation of uridine nucleotides in the staphylococcus [8] and, consequently, to the fixation of uracil which is a limiting requirement for anaerobic growth of this organism.[57] β-Galactosidase formation in the staphylococcus is dependent on the addition of uracil and other ribonucleic acid precursors to the incubation medium, and it is possible that penicillin limits the formation of the enzyme by side-tracking uracil. Strominger [58] put forward a similar explanation for the effect of penicillin in inhibiting ribonucleic acid synthesis. Hancock (private communication) has not been able to reverse the action of penicillin on β-galactosidase formation by addition of uracil to the medium. However, it seems possible that β-galactosidase is a membrane enzyme in the staphylococcus; this would account for the inability to get the enzyme into a soluble state [55] and also for its formation in disrupted cell preparations.[56] The action of penicillin on both permeases and β-galactosidase may then be a secondary effect of the disorganisation of the membrane. In this connection it is interesting to recall that penicillin inhibits the formation of nitratase in a Gram-negative bacterium and that the effect is prevented by the presence of $0.2M$ NaCl.[59] In 1949 when this result was obtained, it was stated that "no explanation of the effects described can be put forward at the present time. . . . It seems probable that the treatment with penicillin produces some alteration in the surface of the cell, which is reversed by salt solution, and which is reflected in a slowing of the rate of adaptation to nitrate." Unfortunately we did not consider this result worth following up!

We come back to the inhibition of cell wall synthesis as the most important effect of the presence of penicillin. We still do not understand the mechanism of cell wall synthesis. The work of Crathorn and Hunter [49] suggests that this synthesis takes place in the membrane so that the site of action of penicillin would presumably also be in the membrane, a suggestion that is supported by the binding of penicillin by lipoprotein particles probably derived from the membrane, demonstrated by Cooper.[60]

The Internal Structure of the Cell

Cytoplasmic Granules. From examination of electron micrographs of sections it would appear that the bacterial

cytoplasm contains large numbers of close-packed granules
10–20 mμ in diameter. Granules of similar dimensions
can be obtained by high speed centrifugation of disintegrated cells or lysed protoplasts. Schachman, Pardee, and
Stanier [61] described the ultracentrifugal separation of three
types of granule from disintegrated bacteria of various species. They found that the bulk of the ribonucleic acid was
associated with granules of diameter 10–15 mμ sedimenting
at 40 S. DNA was left in the supernatant after removal of
these granules. More recent studies by Tissières and Watson [62] have shown that the degree of aggregation of the
granules is markedly affected by the magnesium concentration. When broken cells are extracted with 5–10 mM
Mg^{++}, the main type of granule sediments at 100 S; at
lower magnesium concentrations disaggregation occurs with
the appearance of granules sedimenting at 70, 51, and 32 S.
The 70 S particle is an aggregate of one 51 S and one 32 S
particle, while the 100 S particle is apparently an aggregate
of two 70 S particles. Analysis shows all the particles to
consist of 60–65% ribonucleic acid and 40–35% protein, so
that they are essentially pure ribonucleoprotein structures.
The granules appear to be similar to the microsomes described in other tissues, although the latter contain lipid
material in addition to ribonucleoprotein. Earlier investigations of the bacterial granules indicated that various enzymes were associated with the preparations but Tissières
and Watson [62] point out that the earlier preparations were
not homogeneous and may have contained material derived
from larger structures such as the membrane, so that it is
possible that the oxidising activities previously reported for
the granules may have been due to contaminating materials.
The ribonucleoprotein of the microsomes of animal and
plant cells is believed to be the site of protein synthesis,[63, 64]
but Spiegelman [51] reports that the ribonucleoprotein gran-

ules separated from protoplasts of *Escherichia coli* are not
able to effect protein synthesis although they carry amino
acid "activating enzymes" and will incorporate amino acids
into material insoluble in cold trichloroacetic acid but soluble in hot 5% trichloroacetic acid. Connell and co-workers [52] report that ribonucleoprotein particles isolated from
Azotobacter can incorporate labelled amino acids to a specific activity 10–15% of that attained by the membrane
fraction; the incorporation is dependent upon ATP, is hot
trichloroacetic acid-precipitable, and markedly increased by
the presence of a boiled preparation of the wall/membrane
fraction.

The Nucleus. Considerable controversy has existed
among cytologists concerning the nature and structure of
the bacterial nucleus. Staining reactions, always difficult
to interpret, have produced very variable results that have
served to show, if anything, that the bacterial nucleus must
have an organisation different from that of higher cells.
The electron microscope shows that the central "nuclear
area" of the cell differs in composition from the peripheral
substance, but no differentiating membrane between "nucleus" and "cytoplasm" has been described. Spiegelman,
Aronson, and Fitz-james [65] have described a preparation of
nuclear bodies from lipase-digested protoplasts of *Bacillus
megaterium* and find that they consist of strands of deoxyribonucleic acid gel coiled around a ribonucleoprotein core
or membrane; no membrane can be demonstrated around
the deoxyribonucleic acid itself. There is consequently
intimate association between the deoxyribonucleic acid and
the cytoplasm, and the variable appearance of the "nucleus"
after fixation and staining procedures is explained by the
absence of a limiting membrane imposing morphological
rectitude on the nuclear substance. To what extent the

deoxyribonucleic acid ramifies within the cytoplasm is a matter for present debate and future investigation. Our present knowledge would indicate, however, that there is a simpler organisation of the relationship between deoxyribonucleic acid, cytoplasmic constituents, and cytoplasmic membrane in bacteria than in higher cells.

The Bacterial Cell

The last ten years have seen great advances in our knowledge of the appearance of the bacterial cell, so that we can now begin to understand the nature of some of its parts and their functions. The cell is contained within a strong and rigid wall which protects and stabilises a delicate lipoprotein membrane enclosing protoplasm which is metabolically similar to that found in other living creatures. The organisation of the protoplasm appears at present to be less complex than that of multicellular organisms, and there are suggestions that the distribution of enzymic activities among membrane, granules, and soluble proteins may be different from that now accepted for mammalian cells. Our understanding of the surface structures is better than that of the underlying components, and it is in the specificity of these surface structures that we can look for the sites of action of selective and differential agents. The membrane has both active and passive properties which not only are essential for the maintenance of the internal conditions of the cell but also appear to play an important rôle in the integration of the biochemistry of the cell which allows it to exist as a living unit. The far-reaching consequences of interference with the structure of either membrane or wall demonstrate the over-riding importance of the morphological organisation of the cell.

The bacterial cell thus provides an admirable medium

for the development of the biochemist whether he be concerned with the nature of differentiation or the fundamentals of life.

REFERENCES

1. Dawson, I. M., *Symposium Soc. Gen. Microbiol.*, **1**, 119 (1949).
2. Houwink, A. L., *Biochim. et Biophys. Acta*, **10**, 363 (1953).
3. Salton, M. R. J., and Williams, R. C., *Biochim. et Biophys. Acta*, **14**, 454 (1954).
4. Salton, M. R. J., *Symposium Soc. Gen. Microbiol.*, **6**, 81 (1956).
5. Mitchell, P. D., and Moyle, J., *J. Gen. Microbiol.*, **5**, 981 (1951).
6. Cummins, C. S., and Harris, H., *J. Gen. Microbiol.*, **14**, 583 (1956).
7. Park, J. T., *Symposium Soc. Gen. Microbiol.*, **8**, 49 (1958).
8. Park, J. T., *J. Biol. Chem.*, **194**, 877, 885, 897 (1952).
9. Park, J. T., and Strominger, L., *Science*, **125**, 99 (1957).
10. Armstrong, J. J., Baddiley, J., Buchanan, J. C., Carss, B., and Greenberg, G. R., *J. Chem. Soc.*, **1958**, 4344.
11. Brumfitt, W., Wardlaw, C., and Park, J. T., *Nature*, **181**, 1783 (1958).
12. Weibull, C., *J. Bacteriol.*, **66**, 696 (1953).
13. Mitchell, P. D., and Moyle, J., *Symposium Soc. Gen. Microbiol.*, **6**, 150 (1956).
14. Brenner, S., Dark, F. A., Gerhardt, P., Jeynes, M. H., Kandler, O., Kellenberger, E., Klieneberger-Nobel, E., McQuillen, K., Rubio-Huertos, M., Salton, M. R. J., Strange, R. E., Tomcsik, J., and Weibull, C., *Nature*, **181**, 1713 (1958).
15. Meadow, P., Hoare, D. S., and Work, E., *Biochem. J.*, **66**, 270 (1957).
16. McQuillen, K., *J. Gen. Microbiol.*, **18**, 498 (1958).
17. Buchanan, J. G., Greenberg, G. R., Carss, B., Armstrong, J. J., and Baddiley, J., *4th Intern. Congr. Biochem.*, *1958, Abstr.*, 7.
18. Ledeberg, J., *Proc. Natl. Acad. Sci. U.S.*, **42**, 574 (1956).
19. Hahn, F. E., and Ciak, J., *Science*, **125**, 119 (1957).
20. McQuillen, K., *4th Intern. Congr. Biochem.*, *1958* (in press).
21. Hancock, R., *Biochem. J.*, **70**, 15P (1958).
22. Gale, E. F., and Folkes, J. P., *Biochem. J.*, **53**, 493 (1953); **55**, 721 (1953).
23. Paine, T. F., *J. Bacteriol.*, **61**, 259 (1951).

24. Abraham, E. P., *Biochemistry of Some Peptide and Steroid Antibiotics,* Wiley, New York, 1957, p. 81.

25. Ciak, J., and Hahn, F. E., *Bacteriol. Proc.,* **P40,** 108 (1958); Rubio-Huertos, M., and Desjardius, P. R., *Microbiol. españ.,* **9,** 375 (1956); Jeynes, M. H., *Nature,* **180,** 867 (1957); Welsch, M., and Schweiz, Z., *Allgem. Pathol. u. Bakteriol.,* **21,** 741 (1958).

26. Mandelstam, J., and Rogers, H. J., *Nature,* **181,** 956 (1958).

27. Hancock, R., and Park, J. T., *Nature,* **181,** 1050 (1958).

28. Park, J. T., *Biochem. J.,* **70,** 2P (1958).

29. Gilby, A. R., Few, A. V., and McQuillen, K., *Biochim. et Biophys. Acta,* **29,** 21 (1958).

30. Weibull, C., and Bergstrom, L., *Biochim. et Biophys. Acta,* **30,** 340 (1958).

31. Mitchell, P. D., and Moyle, J., *Biochem. J.,* **64,** 19P (1956).

32. Gale, E. F., *J. Gen. Microbiol.,* **1,** 53 (1947).

33. Taylor, E. S., *J. Gen. Microbiol.,* **1,** 86 (1947).

34. Hotchkiss, R. D., *Advances in Enzymol.,* **4,** 153 (1954).

35. Salton, M. R. J., *J. Gen. Microbiol.,* **5,** 391 (1951).

36. Weibull, C., *Symposium Soc. Gen. Microbiol.,* **6,** 111 (1956).

37. McQuillen, K., *Symposium Soc. Gen. Microbiol.,* **6,** 127 (1956).

38. Gale, E. F., and Taylor, E. S., *J. Gen. Microbiol.,* **1,** 77 (1947).

39. Newton, B. A., *J. Gen. Microbiol.,* **9,** 54 (1953).

40. Newton, B. A., *J. Gen. Microbiol.,* **10,** 491 (1954).

41. Newton, B. A., *J. Gen. Microbiol.,* **12,** 226 (1955).

42. Newton, B. A., *Bacteriol. Rev.,* **20,** 14 (1956).

43. Bell, P. H., Bone, J. F., English, J. P., Fellows, C. E., Howard, K. S., Rogers, M. M., Shepherd, R. G., Winterbottom, R., Dormbush, A. C., Kishner, S., and SubbaRow, Y., *Ann. N. Y. Acad. Sci.,* **51,** 897 (1949).

44. Schwyzer, R., in CIBA Symposium, *Amino Acids and Peptides with Antimetabolic Activities,* Churchill, London, 1958, p. 171.

45. Cohen, G. N., and Monod, J., *Bacteriol. Rev.,* **21,** 169 (1957).

46. Cohen, G. N., and Rickenberg, H. V., *Ann. Inst. Pasteur,* **91,** 693 (1956).

47. Spiegelman, S., in *The Chemical Basis of Heredity* (eds. McElroy, W. D., and Glass, B.), Johns Hopkins Press, Baltimore, 1956, p. 232.

48. Butler, J. A. V., Crathorn, A. R., and Hunter, G. D., *Biochem. J.,* **69,** 544 (1958).

49. Crathorn, A. R., and Hunter, G. D., *Biochem. J.,* **69,** 47P (1958).

50. Beljanski, M., and Ochoa, S., *Proc. Natl. Acad. Sci. U.S.*, **44,** 496 (1958).

51. Spiegelman, S., *Recent Progress in Microbiology,* Almqvist & Wiksell, Stockholm, 1959, p. 81.

52. Connell, G. E., Lengyel, P., and Warner, R. C., *Biochim. et Biophys. Acta,* **31,** 391 (1959).

53. Gale, E. F., and Taylor, E. S., *J. Gen. Microbiol.,* **1,** 314 (1947).

54. Brown, J. W., and Binkley, S. B., *J. Biol. Chem.,* **221,** 579 (1956).

55. Creaser, E. H., *J. Gen. Microbiol.,* **12,** 288 (1955).

56. Gale, E. F., and Folkes, J. P., *Biochem. J.,* **59,** 675 (1955).

57. Richardson, G. M., *Biochem. J.,* **30,** 2184 (1936).

58. Strominger, J. L., *J. Biol. Chem.,* **224,** 525 (1957).

59. Gale, E. F., *Brit. J. Exptl. Pathol.,* **30,** 356 (1949).

60. Cooper, P. D., *Bacteriol. Rev.,* **20,** 28 (1956).

61. Schachman, H. K., Pardee, A. B., and Stanier, R. Y., *Arch. Biochem. Biophys.,* **38,** 245 (1952).

62. Tissières, A., and Watson, J. D., *Nature,* **182,** 778 (1958).

63. Littlefield, J. W., Keller, E. B., Gross, J., and Zamecnik, P. C., *J. Biol. Chem.,* **217,** 111 (1955).

64. Webster, G. C., and Johnson, M. P., *J. Biol. Chem.,* **217,** 641 (1955).

65. Spiegelman, S., Aronson, A. I., and Fitz-james, P. C., *J. Bacteriol.,* **75,** 102 (1958).

2

AMINO ACID INCORPORATION

> Only such substances can be anchored at any
> particular place in the organism which can
> fit into the molecule of the recipient combi-
> nation as a piece of mosaic fits into a certain
> pattern.
>
> **Paul Ehrlich**

It has been known for many years that incubation of an
isotopically labelled amino acid with a biological preparation frequently results in fixation of the isotope by the preparation. The pioneer studies of Borsook [1] and his colleagues established that, for a variety of cells and tissue
preparations, the fixation of the isotope could be attributed
to incorporation of the labelled amino acid into the protein
of the preparation. Tests showed that the incorporated
amino acid was inseparable from the protein fraction and
was liberated from it only by procedures which resulted in
hydrolysis of the protein; if the hydrolysis was partial, the
labelled amino acid was found as a component of several
different peptides. From such evidence it was deduced that

the incorporated residue had become part of the structure of the protein. Since then the fixation of labelled amino acids by protein fractions has frequently been used as an indication of, and a measure of, protein synthesis.

Amino acid incorporation of this nature can often be demonstrated when cells are incubated with a single amino acid although those cells are known to require a battery of amino acids (which may amount to a complete mixture of the naturally occurring ones) before they can synthesise protein. This has led me,[2] among others, to suggest that studies of the incorporation of a single amino acid may not be suitable for investigations of protein synthesis *per se* unless that synthesis can be confirmed by other methods. Our own studies have been carried out with a strain of *Staphylococcus aureus* which is unable to synthesise cellular protein unless a mixture of some 18 amino acids is supplied and yet incubation of intact or disrupted cells with a source of energy and a single amino acid (condition 1) results in a rapid incorporation of that amino acid into the trichloroacetic acid-insoluble fraction of the cells. The rate and time-course of this incorporation is different from that occurring when the full complement of 18 amino acids is present (condition 2) and protein synthesis can be demonstrated by an increase in protein-L-glutamic acid or enzyme activity.[2–4]

Investigations taking place during the last two years have shown that fixation of amino acids may involve substances other than true protein. In experiments involving Gram-positive bacteria, incorporation may take place into the incomplete protein or peptide of the wall structure as described in the previous chapter. Table 6 shows that the major part of the incorporation of glutamic acid, glycine, alanine, or lysine that takes place with intact staphylococci incubated under condition 1 in the presence of glucose re-

TABLE 6

Incorporation of Amino Acids by Intact and Disrupted Staphylococcal Cells; Proportion of Incorporated Activity Associated with Cell Wall Fraction [5]

Amino Acid	Specific Activity, counts/ min./ mμmole	Incorporation in Intact Cells		Incorporation in Disrupted Cells	
		Counts/min. TCA ppt.	% Radioactivity in Wall Fraction	Counts/min. TCA ppt.	% Radioactivity in Wall Fraction
Glutamic acid	1340	6165	71	1249	13
Glycine	534	5458	91	1081	40
Lysine	1710	5391	51	2375	20
Alanine	431	2882	70	371	25
Valine	1175	2221	13	1092	9
Leucine	1170	2470	13	1257	12

All incubations under condition 1; intact cells in presence of glucose, disrupted cells in presence of ATP as source of energy; quantities in ref. 5.

fers to the cell wall fraction.[5] If the cells have been disrupted by treatment with supersound, then incorporation still takes place under condition 1 but a much smaller proportion of that incorporation refers to the wall fraction; incorporation into the wall fraction becomes insignificant if supersound treatment has been continued for a sufficient time.

The work of Hoagland and his colleagues [6] has also revealed that amino acids can be fixed by "soluble ribonucleic acid (rna)." In this case the fixation is through reversible, alkali-labile, ribonuclease-sensitive bonds to polyribonucleotide-containing material which is soluble in hot trichloroacetic acid but precipitable by cold 5% (w/v) trichloroacetic acid. The soluble ribonucleic acid is a heterogeneous material in which the molecular size and specificity of the acceptor for amino acids have not yet been determined. Incorporation by soluble *rna* can be distinguished from incorporation into protein by precipitation of the latter by hot trichloroacetic acid. Consequently, if the fixation of an amino acid is not affected by extraction by hot trichloroacetic acid, then the incorporation cannot be attributed to soluble *rna*; this statement assumes that the amino acid residues released by hydrolysis of the soluble *rna* will not react with, or be adsorbed by, trichloroacetic acid-precipitable components of the preparation, and this is a possibility that cannot as yet be ruled out.[7]

Extraction with hot trichloroacetic acid thus provides a fractionation into nucleic acid-like and protein-like acceptors, and it is next necessary to decide whether trichloroacetic acid-precipitable acceptors are proteins. Protein synthesis can only occur if all the necessary amino acids are available, and, consequently, the incorporation of a single amino acid into protein should be markedly affected by the presence or absence of the others. Figure 7 shows, for example, the different time-course for the incorporation of glutamic acid by staphylococci under conditions 1 and 2; it can be seen that linear incorporation takes place only in the presence of the complete amino acid mixture. The synthesis of incomplete proteins will be discussed below. At one time it was thought that evidence concerning the nature of incorporation could be obtained by the use of amino acid analogues. Thus Spiegelman and his colleagues showed that the formation of enzymes could be prevented by the presence of *p*-fluorophenylalanine or azatryptophan,[8, 9] but the recent studies of Munier and Cohen [10] have shown that such analogues are incorporated into protein molecules in place of the corresponding natural amino acids so that "protein" synthesis continues although the products are enzymically inactive. Such analogues cannot therefore be used to assist the interpretation of incorporation studies unless it has first been proved that the analogues in question do inactivate the protein-synthesising mechanism.

Chloramphenicol inhibits the synthesis of enzymes in bacteria, and Table 3 (p. 15) shows that it almost completely suppresses the incorporation of glutamic acid into the protein fraction of intact staphylococci incubated under condition 2. Reports of the action of chloramphenicol in animal systems are variable, and no clear-cut statement whether it affects protein synthesis or amino acid incorporation in cell-free preparations can be made as yet.[11–13] The incorporation of amino acids that takes place into the staphylococcal cell wall is chloramphenicol-resistant,[14, 15] but cell wall fractions may contain material from the protoplast membrane, and chloramphenicol-resistant incorporation into the protein of such fractions has also been reported.[16, 17] Incorporation of amino acids, even of those not associated with wall peptides, into the "protein" fraction of staphylococci incubated under condition 1 is never completely suppressed by chloramphenicol but displays a variable resistant portion. Presumably the further investigation of the nature of the sensitive and resistant fractions will throw light on the mechanism of protein synthesis in the bacterial cell. For the present, however, there are *a priori* grounds for believing that a process is involved in protein synthesis if it is inhibited by chloramphenicol, although, until the mode of action of the antibiotic is elucidated, it does not follow that it is the formation of protein itself, rather than a complex precursor, that is concerned.

Amino acid incorporation is thus a valuable tool for use in the investigation of protein synthesis. However, it is still desirable to demonstrate a net increase in true protein before there can be certainty that amino acid incorporation is a measure of protein synthesis.

Amino Acid Requirements and Protein Synthesis

It has become almost axiomatic that protein synthesis will not take place unless all the naturally occurring amino acids are provided, and it is general experience that an amino acid-requiring mutant cannot form protein unless the requirement is met. However, some proteins occur which do not contain the full complement of amino acids (examples in the animal kingdom are insulin and haemoglobin) and the question arises whether such incomplete proteins can be formed under more restricted conditions than are necessary for general protein synthesis. The proteins of bacterial flagella are incomplete [18] and have the advantage that their formation can be studied both by direct microscopic observation and also by their ability to impart motility. Furthermore, it is possible to deflagellate some bacteria by subjecting them to shearing forces in a suitable mixer, and the cells possess the ability to regenerate flagella during incubation under suitable conditions. The flagellin of *Salmonella typhimurium* is devoid of tryptophan, cysteine, and hydroxyproline,[19] and Kerridge [20] has investigated the ability of a number of mutant strains of this organism to synthesise protein and regenerate flagella under defined conditions. He finds that tryptophan- or cysteine-requiring mutants cannot synthesise cellular protein in the absence of the relevant amino acid but can nevertheless regenerate functional flagella (see Plate IV). A leucine-less mutant, however, can neither synthesise protein nor regenerate flagella in the absence of added leucine. The regeneration is prevented by the presence of chloramphenicol.

Two interesting side issues have arisen from this work. The salmonella flagellin contains amounts of histidine and methionine corresponding to 1 molecule of amino acid per

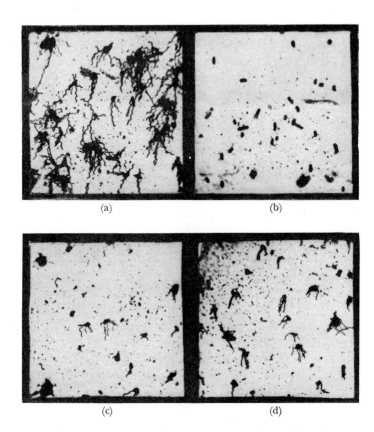

(a)   (b)

(c)   (d)

Plate IV. Regeneration of flagella by *Salmonella typhimurium* (*ca.* ×500). (a) Normal flagellated cells; (b) cells after removal of flagella; (c) cells in the course of regeneration of flagella; (d) cells with flagella formed in the presence of *p*-fluorophenylalanine. By courtesy of Dr. D. Kerridge (University of Cambridge).

protein unit of molecular weight 30,000, and histidine- or methionine-requiring mutants, although unable to synthesise cellular protein in the absence of the required amino acid, can nevertheless regenerate flagella. It seems possible that the small requirement for histidine or methionine can be met by turnover of the cellular protein. Munier and Cohen [10] have shown that *Escherichia coli* can utilise *p*-fluorophenylalanine in place of phenylalanine for the synthesis of protein but that such replacement results in the formation of inactive proteins. Flagellin contains phenylalanine, and, if cells are allowed to regenerate flagella in the presence of *p*-fluorophenylalanine, Kerridge [21] finds that abnormal "curly" flagella (see Plate IV) are produced and the organisms are non-motile.

Amino Acid Incorporation in Animal Tissues

When a labelled amino acid is supplied to mammalian cells, pulse experiments show that the label is first taken up by the microsomes and then passed on to the soluble protein fraction of the cells.[22, 23] Isolated microsomes are able to incorporate labelled amino acids if the incubation mixture contains adenosine triphosphate (ATP) or phosphoglycerate and a fraction of the supernatant cytoplasm which is precipitated at pH 5.[6, 22, 24, 25] The pH 5 precipitated fraction contains enzymes which are capable of carrying out an exchange reaction between ATP and pyrophosphate in the presence of specific amino acids:

$$\alpha + \text{ATP} \rightleftharpoons \alpha\text{-AMP} + \text{PP}$$

(AMP = adenosine monophosphate; PP = pyrophosphate). The pH 5 precipitate also contains "soluble ribonucleic acid" (*rna*), and incubation of the fraction with ATP and an amino acid results in the amino acid becoming bound as an amino acyl-*rna* complex. It is assumed that the adenyl-amino acid (α-AMP) is an intermediate in the binding process which can be formulated as

$$\alpha\text{-AMP} + rna \rightleftharpoons \alpha\text{-}rna \; (+\text{AMP})$$

or

$$\alpha\text{-AMP} + rna \rightleftharpoons \alpha\text{-AMP-}rna$$

depending upon whether the AMP residue is eliminated or incorporated as an end group to the *rna* molecule. Soluble *rna* can only bind amino acid residues when the polyribonucleotide chain possesses a specific end configuration. If the pH 5 fraction from ascites tumour cells is incubated in the absence of nucleoside triphosphates, the *rna* cannot then serve as acceptor for amino acids unless both ATP and cytidine triphosphate (CTP) are present, and it is believed that the active polynucleotide acceptor must end with a dicytidyl-adenylic acid end group.[26, 27] The amino acyl-*rna* bond is very labile to alkali, while treatment with ribonuclease releases the amino acyl residue as the corresponding amino acyl-adenosine,[28] so that the reaction may be represented as shown below. "Soluble *rna*" has not yet

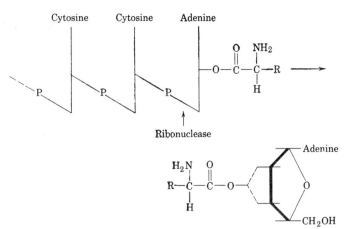

been characterised in detail; its molecular weight is reported to be 5000–10,000, and the material is heterogeneous in the centrifuge. In liver homogenates, the *rna* is precipitated in the pH 5 precipitable fraction, but in preparations from pigeon pancreas the acceptor remains in the pH 5 supernatant.[29] Whether there is specificity between the polyribonucleotide and the amino acid it binds is not yet known. Berg and Ofengand [30] have shown that, when two or more amino acids are added to the system, the binding is additive so that it appears probable that each amino acid is bound at a specific site. It is not known, however, whether one polynucleotide can react with more than one amino acid; if specificity exists, it must presumably be imposed by the sequence of nucleotides adjacent to the end group shown in the reaction above.

The amino acyl-*rna* is believed to act as a carrier of amino acyl residues from the "activating enzymes" (the enzymes bringing about the formation of α-AMP in the presence of ATP) to the site of peptide bond formation in the microsome. The mammalian microsome is a lipo-ribo-nucleo-protein complex, and peptide bond formation occurs when the amino acyl residue is incorporated into the ribo-nucleoprotein (RNP). Zamecnik and his colleagues have found that guanosine triphosphate is necessary for the transfer of the amino acyl residue from the soluble *rna* to the microsomal particle.[25] The sequence of transfers so far elucidated can therefore be represented as in the reaction shown below. One of the major problems involved in pro-

$$\alpha \;+\; \text{ATP} \rightleftharpoons \alpha\text{-AMP} \xrightarrow[\quad rna \quad]{} \alpha\text{-}rna \xrightarrow{\quad} \xrightarrow[\quad RNP \quad]{\text{GTP}} (\alpha\text{-}\alpha)_n\text{-} \text{RNP}$$

tein synthesis is the mechanism of determination of specific amino acid sequences. These sequences are presumably determined by the time a residue is incorporated into the microsomal ribonucleoprotein, but, so far, we have no experimental evidence concerning the mechanism of determination. One of the outstanding questions concerning the system that has been worked out so far is whether any form of sequence determination or specificity holds at the soluble *rna* stage; the answer presumably awaits more definitive methods of separating and characterising the polynucleotide components of the *rna* complex.

Amino Acid Incorporation by Subcellular Preparations from Bacteria

In Chapter 1 a survey was given of various reports relating to the site of protein synthesis in the bacterial cell, and it was pointed out that there is no definite evidence, as yet, that the ribonucleoprotein granules of the bacterial cytoplasm are able to incorporate amino acids, but there are several indications that the protoplast membrane is involved in protein synthesis. Spiegelman[31] has broken protoplasts of *Escherichia coli* and separated three fractions: the membrane fragments, ribonucleoprotein granules, and soluble protein. He reports that amino acid incorporation into the membrane fragments is dependent upon the presence of the complete mixture of amino acids, takes place in material insoluble in hot trichloroacetic acid, and is inhibited by chloramphenicol. Amino acid incorporation also takes place into the soluble protein and ribonucleoprotein granules, but this incorporation is not dependent upon the presence of other amino acids, is not sensitive to chloramphenicol, and the labelled material is soluble in hot trichloroacetic acid although precipitated by cold trichloroacetic acid. Consequently he believes that protein synthesis is a property of the membrane and not of the ribonucleoprotein granules in the bacterial cell. Pulse experiments have led Butler and co-workers [17,32] to suggest that the protoplast membrane of *Bacillus megaterium* plays a rôle in the early stages of amino acid incorporation into both cellular protein and wall peptides, and Beljanski and Ochoa [33] have investigated the incorporation of amino acids by "membrane fragments" from *Alcaligenes faecalis*. Our own studies have been carried out with staphylococci disrupted by exposure to supersound; the preparation (see Plate V) consists essentially of cells in which the outer structures have been torn and consequently contain wall, membrane, and some residual cytoplasm. The fact that bacteria elaborate a wall structure containing amino acids means that considerable caution has to be exercised in interpreting amino acid incorporation experiments, since the reactions involved may concern protein synthesis, wall synthesis, or both processes. In the Gram-positive organisms, some differentiation is possible since the wall peptide contains few amino acids and the incorporation process is insensitive to chloramphenicol, but no such bases for differentiation have as yet been worked out for Gram-negative organisms and it is not known whether the synthesis of wall protein in these organisms is the same as or different from that of cellular protein.

We shall first investigate the presence in bacterial preparations of biochemical components comparable to those, described above, which are believed to play a rôle in the incorporation of amino acids by animal tissues.

Amino Acid-Activated ATP-Pyrophosphate Exchange. DeMoss and Novelli [34] investigated the ability of extracts of a variety of bacteria to bring about ATP-pyrophosphate exchange in the presence of amino acids. Active extracts were obtained from Micrococci, Aerobacter, Staphylococci, Clostridia, Desulphovibrio, Proteus, Streptococci, Serratia, Rhodospirilla, Azotobacter, and Escherichia species, and

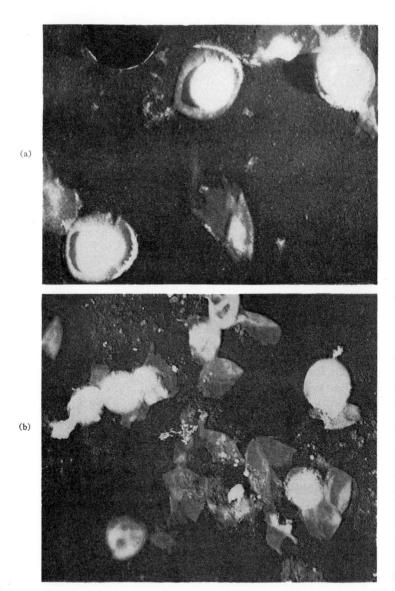

Plate V. Electron micrographs of disrupted staphylococcal cells. (a) Freshly prepared disrupted cells (×18,000); (b) disrupted cells after nucleic acid depletion (×12,000).

46

detailed investigations were made in the case of extracts of *Streptococcus haemolyticus* and *Escherichia coli*. These extracts brought about the exchange reaction in the presence of 8 amino acids: isoleucine, leucine, valine, tyrosine, methionine, phenylalanine, histidine, and tryptophan. Insignificant exchange was promoted by the other 10 amino acids tested. These results are typical of many studies of "amino acid activation" by various tissues, and they pose the problem whether all amino acids are activated in the same way or whether the experimental results are a reflection of varying stability of the different enzymes so that some systems are destroyed in the course of extraction. Lipmann [35] favours the latter explanation and refers to studies with pigeon pancreas extracts which activate 20 amino acids. Table 7 shows the pyrophosphate exchange obtained with disrupted staphylococcal preparations where 11 of the 14 amino acids tested promote a significant increase, the response varying widely according to the amino acid. Glutamic and aspartic acids are interesting exceptions in that all experiments designed to test their "activation" have proved negative, and yet both of these amino acids are rapidly incorporated by the disrupted staphylococci and most of the work to be quoted later in this chapter has been carried out on the incorporation of glutamic acid. Similar results are recorded by Beljanski and Ochoa,[33] who find that their membrane fragment preparation from *Alcaligenes faecalis* will incorporate amino acids but is free from amino acid-dependent pyrophosphate exchange reactions.

Interpretation of these findings is difficult in our present state of knowledge. On the one hand, we have the demonstration that the "pH 5 precipitate" of mammalian and other cells contains enzymes promoting an amino acid-dependent pyrophosphate exchange and that the pH 5 precipitate is necessary for the incorporation of amino acids

TABLE 7

Amino Acid-Activated ATP-Pyrophosphate Exchange in Disrupted Staphylococcal Cells

1.0 mg. dry weight disrupted staphylococcal cells; incubation for 20 min. at $37°$; counts/min. in control without amino acids = 477.

Amino Acid	Increase on Control, counts/min.	% Exchange
Leucine	8,692	6.8
Valine	6,817	5.3
Isoleucine	5,412	4.2
Methionine	4,145	3.25
Cysteine	3,691	2.9
Tyrosine	1,536	1.2
Glycine	542	0.42
Tryptophan	526	0.41
Alanine	384	0.30
Lysine	196	0.15
Histidine	181	0.14
Phenylalanine	23	0.02
Aspartic acid	0	—
Glutamic acid	0	—
Complete mixture of 18 amino acids	18,917	—

by microsomal nucleoprotein. On the other, we have the bacterial preparations in which there is, at least, no clear correlation between ability to incorporate an amino acid and the ability of that amino acid to promote pyrophosphate exchange. It is not known, of course, whether the incorporation of amino acids into bacterial wall structures involves the same components as incorporation into nucleoprotein complexes. Evidence in favour of a rôle in protein synthesis of amino acid "activation" as measured by pyro-phosphate exchange has been obtained by Sharon and Lipmann,[36] who have purified the tryptophan-activating enzyme and found that activation occurs with derivatives, such as 7-azatryptophan, which are incorporated into proteins in place of tryptophan.

Polyribonucleotide Acceptors.   Berg and Ofengand [30] have shown that incubation of amino acids in the presence of ATP, Mg ions, and a dialysed sonic extract of *Escherichia coli* results in the binding of the amino acids to a ribo-nucleic acid-containing fraction.   The binding material is precipitable by cold 5% perchloric acid, and the amino acid is released in an acid-soluble form by treatment with ribo-nuclease or exposure to mild alkali (0.01N NaOH for 5 min. at 25°) or acid hydrolysis (5% perchloric acid for 15 min. at 100°).   The active fraction contains 3% deoxyribonucleic acid, 3–5% protein, and the remainder is ribonucleic acid. Ribonucleic acid preparations from yeast, *Azotobacter vinelandii,* tobacco mosaic virus, and rat liver were unable to substitute for the active fraction from *E. coli.* The amount of amino acid incorporated into the acid-insoluble ribonucleic acid fraction is dependent upon the amount of ribonucleic acid present, and, if several amino acids are added to the medium, then they are incorporated independently and the total radioactivity of the complex equals the sum of the values obtained when the amino acids are added singly.   The incorporation of a given amino acid is dependent upon the presence of the corresponding "activating" enzyme; thus a purified valine-activating enzyme could promote the incorporation of valine only, and the authors suggest that the same enzyme is concerned in the "activation" of the amino acid and in the transfer of that amino acid to ribonucleic acid.   Lacks and Gros [37] have also studied the binding of amino acids by ribonucleic acid in

E. coli and have shown that the binding is reversible, so that the *rna* fraction is continuously undergoing turnover.

Intermediate Acceptors in the Staphylococcus. In our early studies on the incorporation of amino acids by disrupted staphylococcal cells [2] we found that the incorporation of glutamic acid which occurs under condition 1 was partially reversible, and we suggested that this might be explained by an exchange reaction occurring between the added amino acid and corresponding residues in the nucleoprotein. The nature of incorporation under condition 1 has now been investigated in further detail by electrophoresis of nucleoprotein extracts of disrupted cells according to the general technique described by Pardee, Paigen, and Prestidge.[38] Disrupted cells are incubated with labelled substrates in the usual way and then washed exhaustively in water to remove the labelled medium; the washed sediment is then subjected to a further 4–5 min. exposure to supersonic vibration which suffices to disintegrate the residual structure. The disintegrated material is centrifuged at 8000 g for 20 min. to sediment wall fragments, and the supernatant "nucleoprotein extract" is mixed with starch and inserted into a starch bed or column containing $0.05M$ tris buffer of pH 7.6. A potential of 600 v. is applied across a bed 30 cm. long, and electrophoresis is continued for $4\frac{1}{2}$ hr. The bed is then cut into 1-cm. sections, each section eluted in water, and the distribution of nucleic acid (by optical density at 260 mμ) and radioactivity determined. Pardee and co-workers [38] found that the results were affected by the method used for disintegration of the cells and by the nature of the buffer used in the electrophoresis apparatus. The studies of Tissières and Watson,[39] described in Chapter 1, would also indicate that the degree of aggregation of ribonucleoprotein particles can be markedly affected by the conditions of extraction. Consequently the electrophoretic distributions obtained in our experiments may bear little relation to the macromolecular organisation *in vivo*. However, we have found that consistent results are obtained when conditions of disintegration and extraction are standardised, so that major departures from the "normal" distribution probably arise from real changes in the preparation before extraction.

If glutamic acid is incorporated into the disrupted staphylococci under condition 2 and cell extracts are then subjected to electrophoresis in this manner, the radioactivity becomes distributed along the starch column in a manner shown in Fig. 4a. The distribution of glutamyl residues follows that of the nucleic acid with 60% or more of the radioactivity associated with fractions either at the origin or moving not more than 10 cm. toward the anode. If incorporation takes place under condition 1, the resulting distribution of radioactivity is now markedly different, as shown in Fig. 4b; some 80% of the radioactivity is now associated with fast-moving material lying close to the nucleic acid front.

If disrupted staphylococci are incubated with glutamic acid under condition 1, washed, and then incubated a second time with unlabelled glutamic acid and ATP, radioactivity is lost from the fast-moving fractions and can be quantitatively recovered from the supernatant medium. No such loss can be demonstrated by incubating the preparation with ATP alone, or with unlabelled glutamic acid alone. The binding in this fast-moving material is thus reversible in the presence of ATP, but no such reversible incorporation can be demonstrated in the slow-moving fractions. The glutamic acid in the fast-moving material is not in the free state and does not liberate CO_2 on treatment with ninhydrin; it cannot be released by washing or incu-

bating with unlabelled glutamic acid in the absence of
ATP. The formation of the complex is prevented by the
presence, during incubation, of 0.1 mM 1:2-dichloro-
5-nitro-4-(p-nitrobenzenesulphonamido)benzene, which is a

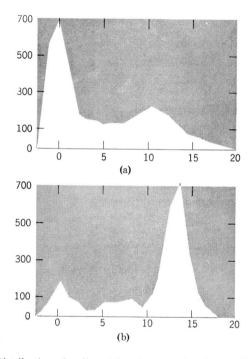

Fig. 4. Distribution of radioactivity along starch columns after electrophoresis of extracts of disrupted staphylococcal cells. Extracts of cells
previously incubated: (a) under condition 2 with ATP and 18 amino
acids including labelled glutamic acid at specific activity of 0.9 mc./
mmole; (b) under condition 1 with ATP and labelled glutamic acid as
sole amino acid added, specific activity = 11.7 mc./mmole. Time = 4½
hr.; potential = 600 v./30 cm.; pH = 7.6 (0.05M tris buffer). Ordinates = radioactivity in counts/min. of eluates from 1-cm. sections of
column. Abscissae = distance, in cm., from origin; movement toward
anode. Details of incubation mixtures, etc., as in ref. 2.

potent inhibitor of incorporation.[40] For the present, the fast-moving component will be referred to as glutamyl-X.

Glutamyl-X is highly unstable; 90% of the glutamic acid is released as the free acid by $0.01N$ KOH in 5 min. at $30°$, by N HCl in 60 min. at $100°$, or by standing at pH 2.0 for 8 hr. at $30°$. Treatment with ribonuclease is incomplete, releasing 30–40% of the glutamyl residues only. The radioactivity is not precipitated by 5% trichloroacetic acid, 5% perchloric acid, or 60% ethanol in the cold, nor is it de-

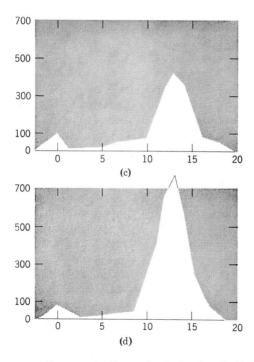

Fig. 4 (Continued). Extracts of cells previously incubated: (c) As (a) but in the presence of 30 μg. chloramphenicol/ml.; (d) as (b) but in the presence of 30 μg. chloramphenicol/ml.

creased by shaking with aqueous phenol. If the glutamic acid released by acid hydrolysis is assayed by the L-glutamic acid decarboxylase,[41] the CO_2 released corresponds to approximately 50% of the glutamic acid being present as the L-isomer. Since the glutamyl residues of the staphylococcal cell wall are present as the D-isomer, it would appear that "glutamyl-X" must be related both to wall and to cellular protein and may accumulate in the preparation since the disrupted staphylococcus can synthesise neither wall nor protein when incubated under condition 1 with ATP as energy source.

The proportion of L-isomer present in glutamyl-X is not significantly affected by the presence of either penicillin or chloramphenicol during incubation, although the variation from the mean value is greatest when chloramphenicol is present. We have attempted to separate glutamyl-X into components by a variety of chromatographic and electrophoretic procedures without success.

The stabilities of glutamyl-X are similar to those reported for the amino acyl-polyribonucleotide complexes described above, but glutamyl-X differs in being soluble in trichloroacetic acid, perchloric acid, and 60% alcohol in the cold. It is clear that glutamyl-X, although the site of reversible incorporation, is not protein in nature. The slow-moving electrophoretic fractions have the properties of nucleoproteins, and no reversible incorporation can be demonstrated in these fractions. Consequently the earlier suggestion that reversible incorporation takes place as a result of exchange between added amino acids and corresponding residues in protein is no longer tenable. The exchangeable incorporation associated with the trichloroacetic acid-precipitable fraction of disrupted cells is much smaller in amount than that in the glutamyl-X fraction and may arise from contamination with glutamyl-X occurring when the trichloroacetic acid treatment is carried out without the prior extraction and electrophoretic separation now employed.

Further investigation of the nature of glutamyl-X is in its early stages, and only preliminary results are available. Advantage has been taken of its solubility in the presence of phenol, and extracts of cells have been shaken with aqueous phenol as for the preparation of soluble *rna*.[24] The deproteinised extract has then been applied to a small column (5 x 1 cm.) of ECTEOLA cellulose, used by Bradley and Rich [42] for the separation of nucleic acid components. Glutamyl-X can be eluted, with retardation of 60–70 ml., by $0.005M$ tris buffer at pH 7.0 or $0.001M$ ammonium formate. Preliminary analyses of the eluted material indicate that it does not contain polynucleotide, but it is not known whether partial breakdown may have occurred during the experimental procedures adopted.

Transfer of Glutamyl Residue to Protein Fraction. If disrupted staphylococci are incubated with glutamic acid and ATP under condition 1, the electrophoretic distribution of the glutamyl residues in the nucleoprotein extracts is as shown in Fig. 4b. If the disrupted cell preparation, after being loaded under condition 1, is washed and reincubated with a complete mixture of amino acids (less glutamic acid) under condition 2, the glutamyl residues undergo redistribution as shown in Fig. 5. Approximately half of the glutamyl-X fraction is transferred to the slow-moving fractions, and the radioactivity so transferred becomes precipitable with hot 5% trichloroacetic acid. Table 8 shows that the transfer is quantitative within experimental error and that there is little incorporation into the wall fraction during the first or second incubation. Estimation of the glutamic acid in the fast-moving fraction before and after the second incubation shows that it is the L-isomer of glutamic acid which is transferred to the protein fractions during incubation under condition 2. It is clear from these experiments that L-glutamyl-X is an intermediate in the incorporation of glutamic acid into protein.

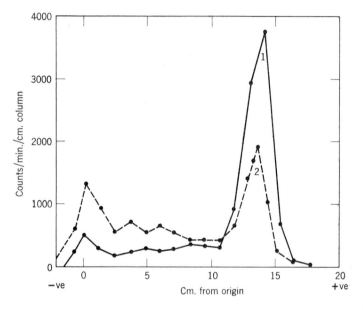

Fig. 5. Redistribution of radioactivity in nucleoprotein extracts of disrupted cells when preparations are incubated (curve 1) under condition 1 with labelled glutamic acid and subsequently (curve 2) under condition 2 in presence of 17 other amino acids. Curve 1, distribution of radioactivity along starch column after electrophoresis (as in Fig. 4) of extracts of cells incubated with ATP and labelled glutamic acid (specific activity 11.7 mc./mmole) for 1 hr. at 37°. Curve 2, preparation as in curve 1, washed and reincubated for 1 hr. at 37° under condition 2 in absence of added glutamic acid. For details see refs. 2 and 5.

TABLE 8

Redistribution of Radioactivity when Disrupted Cells, First Incubated with ^{14}C-Glutamic Acid under Condition 1, Are Reincubated with a Complete Mixture of Amino Acids (less Glutamic Acid) under Condition 2

	Nucleoprotein Extract Electrophoresis on Starch			
	Eluted from cuts 1–12 cm. from Origin	Eluted from cuts 13–16 cm. from Origin	Wall Fraction	Total Count
Condition 1	6,901	19,211	4,200	30,402
Reincubated under condition 2	15,932	10,615	5,256	31,803
Change	+9,031	−8,596	+1,056	+1,401
% change on condition 1 distribution	+131	−45	+25	+5

Action of Chloramphenicol

Chloramphenicol is an inhibitor of protein synthesis in bacteria.[43–47] Many studies have been made of its actions on metabolic processes, and the only process inhibited at growth-limiting concentrations is that of protein synthesis. If staphylococci are incubated under condition 2 in the presence of a growth-limiting concentration (10–30 μg./ml.) of the antibiotic, protein synthesis and the incorporation of an amino acid such as leucine are reduced to less than 5% of that occurring in the absence of chloramphenicol; ribonucleic acid synthesis continues, and the rate of synthesis may be significantly greater than that in the control.[44] If the incorporation of glutamic acid by disrupted staphylococci under conditions 1 and 2 is carried out in the presence of chloramphenicol and the nucleoprotein extracts of the cells then subjected to electrophoresis on starch, the resulting distribution of labelled residues is that shown in Fig. 4, c and d. The distribution under condition 1 is virtually unaffected by the presence of the antibiotic, although the small incorporation normally found in the slow-moving fractions is almost completely suppressed. Under condition 2, however, the antibiotic suppresses incorporation into the slow-moving fractions and effectively converts the distribution into that obtained under condition 1. It would appear from these results that chloramphenicol has no effect upon the binding of glutamic acid under condition 1 (formation of glutamyl-X) but prevents the transfer of glutamyl residues from glutamyl-X to the protein fractions.

Lacks and Gros [37] have shown that binding of amino acids by ribonucleic acid from *Escherichia coli* takes place in the presence or absence of chloramphenicol, although the rate of incorporation of a labelled amino acid, and the rate of its displacement by unlabelled amino acid, is slower in the presence of the antibiotic. The rate of incorporation of a given amino acid is enhanced by prior starvation of the cells toward that amino acid so that vacant acceptor sites may arise during starvation. Chloramphenicol has no inhibitory action on the amino acid-dependent ATP-pyrophosphate exchange [34] or on the reaction between the activated amino acid and ribonucleic acid.[37] From the available evidence it would appear that chloramphenicol prevents the transfer of amino acyl residues from their primary acceptor sites to the peptide-bond-forming site. If this is so, then the presence of chloramphenicol might lead to the accumulation of precursors of protein synthesis and so assist in their characterization. With this object in view, we have incubated disrupted staphylococci with a number of different amino acids, each under condition 1 in the presence of chloramphenicol, and determined the electrophoretic distribution of labelled residues in the nucleoprotein extracts as before. With the exception of leucine and phenylalanine, all the amino acids tested show some chloramphenicol-resistant binding, but the electrophoretic mobility of the labelled component varies with the amino acid concerned. The chloramphenicol-resistant binding of aspartic acid and valine occurs in the same fractions as glutamic acid but, as can be seen from Fig. 6, the corresponding components for other amino acids have slower mobilities under the standard conditions used. The binding of glutamic acid is not affected by the presence of valine (or *vice versa*) but is suppressed by high concentrations of aspartic acid. The binding of valine is markedly affected by the presence of leucine. It would appear that there is specificity between the amino acid and its binding site, but it does not follow that the components revealed in these studies have any biosynthetic rôle as, apart from the difficulties of interpretation inherent in the method (see above), the presence of the antibiotic affects the polymerisation of ribonucleic acid (see Chapter 3), and it is possible that "activated amino acids" might react with abnormal acceptors under such conditions.

Effect of Removing Nucleic Acid on the Ability of Disrupted Staphylococci To Incorporate Amino Acids

Nucleic acid can be removed from the disrupted cell preparation by treatment with ribonuclease or deoxyribonuclease or extraction with M sodium chloride.[2] The extent to which depletion can be effected depends on the time

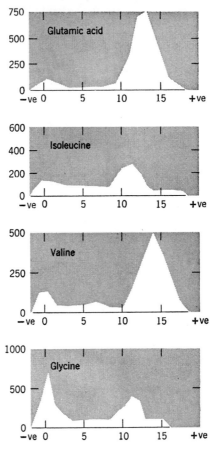

Fig. 6. Distribution of radioactivity along starch columns after electrophoresis of extracts of disrupted staphylococcal cells after incubation with various amino acids under condition 1 (1 amino acid + source of energy) in the presence of chloramphenicol (30 μg./ml.). Ordinates = radioactivity of eluates from 1-cm. sections cut from column. Abscissae = movement, in cm., toward anode during electrophoresis at 20 v./cm. for 4½ hr. at pH 7.6 in 0.05M tris buffer. The diagrams are not strictly comparable as each is obtained from a different extract, but they show the mobilities of the main chloramphenicol-resistant components for each amino acid under condition 1.

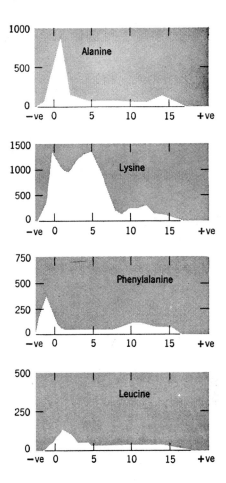

Fig. 6 (Continued). The relevant data for the extracts are as follows:

Amino Acid	Specific Activity, mc./mmole	Approx. Dry Weight of Disrupted Cells Yielding Extract	% Inhibition of Total Condition 1 Incorporation
Glutamic acid	11.7	2.1	15
Isoleucine	7.3	2.8	60
Valine	6.2	3.3	50
Glycine	4.1	2.4	53
Alanine	3.2	1.5	22
Lysine	12.8	3.4	35
Phenylalanine	8.1	2.8	73
Leucine	8.8	1.9	88

for which the cells have been exposed to supersound, most efficient depletion being obtained in preparations in which the cells have been exposed to an extent bordering on complete disintegration. Removal of nucleic acid results in a marked decrease in the ability to incorporate amino acids whether this process is studied under condition 1, 2, or 3. In "good" experiments—usually obtained when the supersonic generator and transducer are working at optimal efficiency—the rate of incorporation of glycine, glutamic acid, leucine (or adenine; see Chapter 3) has been reduced to less than 3% of the rate in undepleted control preparations. The ability to incorporate these amino acids is restored by adding extracted nucleic acid to the incubation mixture. There is no strict specificity in the nucleic acid effect, as nucleic acid extracted from *Staphylococcus aureus, Escherichia coli, Bacillus megaterium,* and baker's yeast has proved active but thymus nucleic acid, DNA from wheat germ or herring roe, and nucleic acid from a strain of *Pseudomonas aeruginosa* have been inactive. A preparation of "soluble *rna*" from liver, supplied by Dr. M. Hoagland, was active. The activity of the bacterial nucleic acids was enhanced by digestion with ribonuclease.

Incorporation Factors. Staphylococcal nucleic acid has been used in most of our studies on the incorporation of amino acids. Digestion of the nucleic acid preparation with ribonuclease approximately doubles its ability to restore incorporation in nucleic acid-depleted cells, and the active material is rendered dialysable during the digestion. Fractionation of the digest led to the isolation of a number of active fractions; at first it was thought that the active materials were oligoribonucleotides, but further fractionation by electrophoretic procedures showed that the active fractions contained substances other than the nucleotides and that the activity lay in these contaminating substances.[47]

Our first experiments were based upon fractionations expected to separate mono-, di-, oligo-, and polynucleotides, but most fractions yielded active contaminants. At that stage, active substances, called "incorporation factors" for convenience, were assayed for their ability to restore the incorporation of a number of different amino acids (under condition 1) in nucleic acid-depleted cells. All active materials had some activity in restoring the incorporation of the amino acids tested but differed in the degree to which they could replace nucleic acid for individual amino acids. Thus one fraction was obtained which would promote the incorporation of glycine and aspartic acid to the same extent as excess nucleic acid but was able to promote the incorporation of valine, isoleucine, glutamic acid, arginine, etc., to an extent only 30–50% of that promoted by nucleic acid. This preparation was called the "glycine incorporation factor." Other factors were obtained from the di- and oligonucleotide fractions of the digest; they all promoted glycine incorporation to the same extent as nucleic acid but differed in the range of amino acids for which the nucleic acid replacement was complete. The meaning of a partial replacement of nucleic acid is not yet understood, but the variations obtained suggest that there is a family of incorporation factors. The quantities of these factors obtained in the early studies was minute, and the fractionation procedure was unsuitable for larger scale work. Consequently a method capable of handling larger amounts of material has been sought and has been used to extract active material from some 20 g. of nucleic acid obtained from *Bacillus megaterium*.[48] The method at present in use involves digestion of the nucleic acid, extraction of active material into ethanol, paper electrophoresis at pH 10.6, and paper chromatography in three systems. Unfortunately

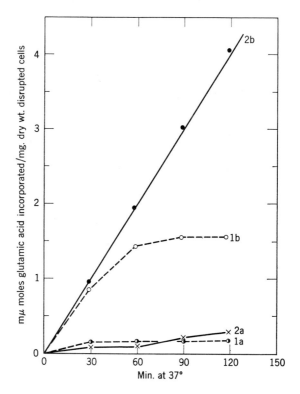

Fig. 7. Effect of the incorporation factor preparation on the incorporation of glutamic acid by disrupted staphylococcal cells.[48] Disrupted cells are depleted of nucleic acid and then incubated with ATP, hexose diphosphate, and C^{14}-labelled glutamic acid. Curve 1a, alone; 1b, with 1 unit incorporation factor added; 2a, under condition 2; 2b, under condition 2 with 1 unit incorporation factor added. Ordinate = glutamic acid incorporated into the hot trichloroacetic acid precipitate of the disrupted cell preparation.

yields are still too small for any useful chemical characterisation to be carried out, and direct knowledge of composition must await preparation on a much larger scale. The incorporation factor preparation made by this method will promote the incorporation of glycine, phenylalanine, aspartic acid, leucine, arginine, glutamic acid, and lysine to the same extent as excess nucleic acid, but it will promote the incorporation of isoleucine, valine, proline, and tyrosine to an extent about half that attained with excess nucleic acid. Whether this preparation is one substance or a mixture is not known. It differs from the original glycine incorporation factor in being destroyed by heating to 100° in N HCl for 1 hr., whereas the glycine factor was not inactivated unless heating was continued for 3 hr. or more.

Figure 7 shows the effect of the presence of the incorporation factor preparation on the course of glutamic acid incorporation into the trichloroacetic acid-precipitable fraction of disrupted staphylococcal cells incubated under conditions 1 and 2. This fraction includes the cell wall material, and, since glutamic acid is one of the components of the wall peptide, it is important to know whether the factor promotes incorporation into both wall and protein. The disrupted cell preparation effects only a small incorporation into wall material, but Table 9 shows that this is affected by the presence of nucleic acid or incorporation factor to the same relative extent as incorporation into the protein fraction. Figure 12 shows the action of the factor preparation on the incorporation of glutamic acid into the various electrophoretic fractions obtained (as described above) from nucleoprotein extracts of disrupted cells incubated under condition 2. It can be seen that the factor promotes incorporation into all fractions, including the fast-moving "glutamyl-X" component, but appears to have

TABLE 9

The Action of Nucleic Acid and "Incorporation Factor" on Incorporation of Glutamic Acid by Disrupted Staphylococcal Cells[5]

	Glutamic Acid Incorporated, μmoles/mg. Disrupted Cells		
	Condition 1		Condition 2
	Wall Fraction	Protein Fraction	Protein Fraction
Disrupted cell preparation depleted of nucleic acid	0.05	0.196	1.50
In presence of 1.0 mg. staphylococcal nucleic acid/3.0 ml.	0.35	0.79	6.71
In presence of 1.0 unit incorporation factor preparation/3.0 ml.	0.30	0.84	7.59

the biggest effect on incorporation into the slower-moving fractions.

Since the factor preparation promotes the incorporation of glutamic acid (and other amino acids) into wall peptides and the various nucleoprotein fractions, it seemed possible that it might be concerned with the primary stages of activation of amino acids. It has not been possible, however, to demonstrate any significant effect of the factor preparation on the amino acid-dependent ATP-pyrophosphate exchange reaction in nucleic acid-depleted staphylococci whether the exchange is promoted by a mixture of 18 amino acids, leucine, valine, or glycine. The factor does not give rise to any exchange in the presence of glutamic acid.

REFERENCES

1. Borsook, H., *Advances in Protein Chem.*, **8**, 128 (1953); *Chemical Pathways of Metabolism*, Vol. II, Academic Press, New York, 1954, p. 173.
2. Gale, E. F., and Folkes, J. P., *Biochem. J.*, **59**, 661, 675 (1955).
3. Gale, E. F., and Folkes, J. P., *Biochem. J.*, **55**, 721 (1953).
4. Gale, E. F., and Folkes, J. P., *Biochem. J.*, **53**, 483 (1953).
5. Gale, E. F., Shepherd, C. J., and Folkes, J. P., *Nature*, **182**, 592 (1958).
6. Hoagland, M. B., *4th Intern. Congr. Biochem., 1958, Symposium on Proteins*, Vol. VIII, Pergamon Press, London, p. 199.
7. Castelfranco, P., and Moldave, K., *Federation Proc.*, **Abstr. 782,** 199 (1958).
8. Halvorson, H. O., and Spiegelman, S., *J. Bacteriol.*, **64**, 207 (1952).
9. Halvorson, H., Spiegelman, S., and Hinman, R. L., *Arch. Biochem. Biophys.*, **55**, 512 (1955).
10. Munier, R., and Cohen, G. N., *Biochim. et Biophys. Acta*, **21**, 592 (1956); *ibid.*, **31**, 347, 379 (1959).
11. Straub, F. B., and Ullman, A., *Biochim. et Biophys. Acta*, **23**, 665 (1957).
12. Allfrey, V. G., Mirsky, A. E., and Osawa, S., *J. Gen. Physiol.*, **40**, 451 (1957).
13. Wagle, S. R., Mehta, R., and Johnson, B. C., *J. Biol. Chem.*, **233**, 619 (1958).
14. Hancock, R., and Park, J. T., *Nature*, **181**, 1050 (1958).
15. Mandelstam, J., and Rogers, H. J., *Nature*, **181**, 956 (1958).
16. Park, J. T., *Biochem. J.*, **70**, 2P (1958).
17. Crathorn, A. R., and Hunter, G. D., *Biochem. J.*, **69**, 47P (1958).
18. Koffler, H., *Bacteriol. Rev.*, **21**, 227 (1957).
19. Ambler, R. P., and Rees, M. W., *Nature*, **184**, 56 (1959).
20. Kerridge, D., *J. Gen. Microbiol.*, **21**, 168 (1959).
21. Kerridge, D., *Biochim. et Biophys. Acta*, **31**, 579 (1959).
22. Littlefield, J. W., Keller, E. B., Gross, J., and Zamecnik, P. C., *J. Biol. Chem.*, **217**, 111 (1955).
23. Rabinowitz, M., and Olson, M. E., *Exptl. Cell Research*, **10**, 747 (1956).

24. Hoagland, M. B., Zamecnik, P. C., and Stephenson, M. L., *Biochim. et Biophys. Acta,* **24,** 215 (1957).

25. Hoagland, M. B., Stephenson, M. L., Scott, J. F., Hecht, L. I., and Zamecnik, P. C., *J. Biol. Chem.,* **231,** 241 (1958).

26. Hecht, L. I., Zamecnik, P. C., Stephenson, M. L., and Scott, J. F., *J. Biol. Chem.,* **233,** 954 (1958).

27. Hecht, L. I., Stephenson, M. L., and Zamecnik, P. C., *Federation Proc.,* **17,** 239 (1958).

28. Zachau, H. G., Acs, G., and Lipmann, F., *Proc. Natl. Acad. Sci. U.S.,* **44,** 885 (1958).

29. Weiss, S. B., Acs, G., and Lipmann, F., *Proc. Natl. Acad. Sci. U.S.,* **44,** 189 (1958).

30. Berg, P., and Ofengand, E. J., *Proc. Natl. Acad. Sci. U.S.,* **44,** 78 (1958).

31. Spiegelman, S., *Recent Progress in Microbiology,* Almqvist & Wiksell, Stockholm, 1959, p. 81.

32. Butler, J. A. V., Crathorn, A. R., and Hunter, G. D., *Biochem. J.,* **69,** 544 (1958).

33. Beljanski, M., and Ochoa, S., *Proc. Natl. Acad. Sci. U.S.,* **44,** 496 (1958).

34. DeMoss, J. A., and Novelli, G. D., *Biochim. et Biophys. Acta,* **18,** 592 (1955).

35. Lipmann, F., *Proc. Natl. Acad. Sci. U.S.,* **44,** 67 (1958).

36. Sharon, N., and Lipmann, F., *Arch. Biochem. Biophys.,* **69,** 219 (1957).

37. Lacks, S., and Gros, F., *J. Molecular Biol.* (in press).

38. Pardee, A. B., Paigen, K., and Prestidge, L. S., *Biochim. et Biophys. Acta,* **23,** 162 (1957).

39. Tissières, A., and Watson, J. D., *Nature,* **182,** 778 (1958).

40. Gale, E. F., and Folkes, J. P., *Biochem. J.,* **67,** 507 (1957).

41. Gale, E. F., *Methods of Biochem. Anal.,* **4,** 285 (1957).

42. Bradley, D. F., and Rich, A., *J. Am. Chem. Soc.,* **78,** 5898 (1956).

43. Hahn, F. E., and Wisseman, C. L., *Proc. Soc. Exptl. Biol. Med.,* **76,** 533 (1951).

44. Gale, E. F., and Folkes, J. P., *Biochem. J.,* **53,** 483, 493 (1953).

45. Wisseman, C. L., Smadel, J. E., Hahn, F. E., and Hopps, H. E., *J. Bacteriol.,* **67,** 662, 674 (1954).

46. Gale, E. F., Ciba Symposium, *Amino Acids and Peptides with Antimetabolite Activity,* Churchill, London, 1958, p. 19.

47. Gale, E. F., *Harvey Lectures,* **51,** 25 (1956–57).

48. Gale, E. F., and Folkes, J. P., *Biochem. J.,* **69,** 611 (1958).

3

NUCLEIC ACID
AND PROTEIN SYNTHESIS

> While ruder heads stand amazed at those
> prodigious pieces of nature, as Elephants,
> Dromidaries, and Camels; these I confesse
> are the Colossus and Majestick pieces of her
> hand; but in these narrow Engines there is
> more curious Mathematicks, and the civility
> of these little Citizens, more nearly sets forth
> the wisdome of their Maker.
>
> **Sir Thomas Browne**

Nucleic Acid Synthesis

All free-living self-reproducing organisms possess two
types of nucleic acid: ribonucleic acid (RNA) and deoxyribonucleic acid (DNA). The two nucleic acids differ in
the nature of the pentose and in the bases, RNA containing
adenine, guanine, uracil, and cytosine, and DNA containing
adenine, guanine, cytosine, and thymine. Until three or
four years ago many investigations in the field of protein
synthesis were devoted to demonstrating that nucleic acids
are involved in protein synthesis. Most of the demonstra-

69

tions were indirect and led to the conclusions that (a) DNA is in some way concerned in controlling the sorts of protein made by a cell, (b) RNA has a catalytic function in the synthetic process itself, and (c) protein synthesis is usually accompanied by, and may be dependent on, RNA synthesis. A definite rôle for RNA emerged from the work outlined in the last chapter; in fact, a dual rôle appears to have been established in that the "soluble *rna*" acts as an intermediate carrier of amino acyl residues while macromolecular RNA provides the site on which peptide bond formation takes place.   Many theories have been put forward during the last ten years to account for the requirement for nucleic acid in protein synthesis and the one most generally in favour at the moment proposes that the DNA carries the information necessary for the construction of specific amino acid sequences, that this information is carried by RNA to the position where amino acid residues are made available, and that the amino acids are then condensed in the right sequences as a result of the information carried by the RNA.   Information yielding determined sequences of 20 amino acid units must be "coded" in the DNA, and it is suggested that combinations of nucleotides along the polynucleotide chain provide the code.   It follows from this theory that RNA synthesis must involve a reaction with DNA if the DNA coding is transferred in the form of a similar coding of nucleotides along the RNA chain.   The final stage of sequence determination would then involve lining up of amino acyl residues along the RNA chain as a template.   It is presumably the RNA of the ribonucleoprotein which provides the template, and the rôle of the soluble *rna* has yet to be determined in relation to sequence formation.   The information theory provides a philosophical background for the design and interpretation of experiments but gives little guidance for mechanisms at a molecular level. Experimental work of the last three years has begun to reveal some of the components of the mechanisms but has, as yet, provided little evidence for a relationship of these components to the information theory.

Amino Acid Requirements. One of the most interesting findings concerning RNA synthesis *in vivo* is that it will take place only in the presence of the complete mixture of amino acids required for protein synthesis. Figure 8 shows the synthesis of RNA by *Staphylococcus aureus* incubated with glucose, a mixture of purines and pyrimidines, and various mixtures of amino acids.[1] Optimal synthesis occurs only in the presence of the 18 amino acids required for protein synthesis; omission of one essential amino acid leads to a marked decrease in synthesis. A number of workers have tested the ability of amino acid-requiring mutants to synthesise RNA and have confirmed the general finding that synthesis will take place only when the essential amino acid is supplied.[2–5] This may mean that RNA and protein are co-products of one process or that they are products of different processes with a common precursor of an amino acyl nucleotide nature.[4] Michelson [6] has presented a chemical formulation of "protein" and/or "nucleic acid" synthesis from amino acid anhydrides of 2′,3′ cyclic nucleoside phosphates. The work of Hecht and collaborators,[7] discussed in Chapter 2, has already shown that the incorporation of an amino acid by soluble *rna* is dependent upon a specific nucleotide end sequence, and it may also be that the extension of a polynucleotide chain requires a specific amino acyl nucleotide end group.

Chloramphenicol effects a separation of protein and nucleic acid syntheses in that a growth-limiting concentration of the antibiotic inhibits protein synthesis but is without inhibitory action on RNA synthesis—that latter may, in fact, be stimulated.[8] The synthesis of RNA that takes

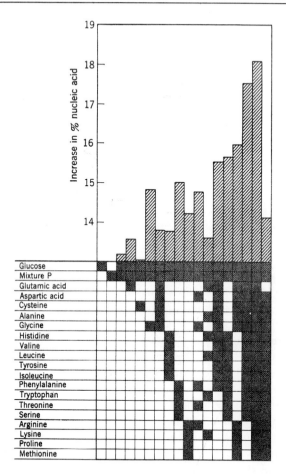

Fig. 8. Effect of amino acids on synthesis of nucleic acid by *Staphylococcus aureus*.[1] Washed suspensions incubated for 1 hr. at 37° in buffered salt medium containing 1% glucose, mixture P = purines and pyrimidines each at a final concentration of 0.02 mg./ml., and amino acids each at 1.34 μmoles/ml. as indicated by black squares.

place in the presence of chloramphenicol is nevertheless dependent upon the presence of amino acids.[5, 9]

Polyribonucleotide Synthesis by Cell-Free Preparations.
Grunberg-Manago, Ortiz, and Ochoa [10] have obtained an enzyme, polynucleotide phosphorylase, from bacterial extracts which brings about a reaction formulated as

$$n(\text{XrP-P}) \rightleftharpoons (\text{XrP})_n + \text{P}$$

where X = adenine, guanine, cytosine, or uracil, XrP = the corresponding ribonucleotide, P = orthophosphate, and P-P = diphosphate. The product $(\text{XrP})_n$ is a polyribonucleotide; if X is adenine then the product is a polyadenylate, whereas if the substrate consists of a mixture of the four diphosphates then the product is a mixed polyribonucleotide with properties similar to those of ribonucleic acid. The purified enzyme requires the presence of magnesium ions and a primer consisting of a small polyribonucleotide (trinucleotide or larger), but no amino acids are necessary nor is there any evidence of a requirement for DNA.

Spiegelman,[11] as described in Chapter 2, has prepared membrane fragments of *Escherichia coli* which are able to accomplish the synthesis of polyribonucleotides. The synthesis differs from that brought about by the polynucleotide phosphorylase of Grunberg-Manago in that it requires nucleoside triphosphates rather than the diphosphates, is activated by Mn and not by Mg, and is dependent on the presence of deoxyribonucleotides for optimal activity. The reaction is inactivated by deoxyribonuclease or the presence of phosphate. The published data [11] do not indicate a requirement for amino acids, but these are present in the incubation medium (Spiegelman, private communication).

What, then, is the relation between nucleic acid synthesis in the intact cell and polyribonucleotide formation by the membrane system of Spiegelman or by polynucleotide phos-

phorylase? It is probable that the product is not of the
same nature in the three systems. If we are to believe the
general thesis that RNA carries information, then it is
difficult to see how any information could be imparted or
imposed by the polynucleotide phosphorylase enzyme unless it were information related to the synthesis of that enzyme. An association with DNA, such as appears in the
membrane system, and a dependence on amino acids are
more easily reconciled with the information theory, and
the conditions which are optimal for polyribonucleotide
synthesis by the membrane system are also those optimal for amino acid incorporation. We have to bear in
mind that there are at least two species of ribonucleic
acid in the cell, and, although we may believe that the
nucleic acid of ribonucleoproteins carries specificity, we do
not know whether this is true of the "soluble *rna*" components; the membrane system and the polynucleotide phosphorylase may be concerned with the elaboration of such
components. The membrane system is inhibited by the
presence of orthophosphate, while polynucleotide phosphorylase brings about the reverse action of phosphorolysis
in the presence of orthophosphate; since the internal medium of the bacterial cell is rich in orthophosphate, it
would appear that polyribonucleotide *synthesis* by these
systems would be suppressed *in vivo*. After all, this would
not be the first time that essentially catabolic systems have
brought about polymerisation reactions under unphysio-
logical conditions *in vitro*. The biochemist has become con-
ditioned to the belief that one must purify an enzyme in
order to study its action, but this belief has arisen from
experience obtained with enzymes dealing with relatively
simple substrates and products and it may not be the best
approach to the synthesis of complex macromolecules. We
are rapidly learning of the complexity of the internal or-

ganisation of living cells, but we have not yet been able to discern the reason for this complexity. Is it something to do with this matter of the synthesis of specific macromolecules in which the *order* of units within the molecule is all important? For such reasons, it is important to learn as much as possible from the complex systems with their wider requirements. And the rest may follow.

Ribonucleic Acid Synthesis in the Staphylococcus. The disrupted staphylococcal cell can synthesise RNA under conditions similar to those required by the intact cells, *viz.,* in the presence of a source of energy and a supply of purines, pyrimidines, ribose and amino acids.[12] The synthesis can be followed by an increase in the optical density at 260 mμ of the nucleic acid fraction or, more readily, by incorporation of labelled purines or pyrimidines into that fraction with the proviso, in the latter case, that an increase in radioactivity does not necessarily measure a net increase in nucleic acid as such. Figure 9 shows the time-course of incorporation of labelled adenine into the nucleic acid fraction of disrupted staphylococci. Incubation with ATP and adenine alone results in little incorporation, although there is some increase in radioactivity of the nucleic acid fraction during the first 30 min. of the incubation period. The addition of a single amino acid such as glutamic acid has little or no effect upon this basal incorporation. In the presence of a mixture of 18 amino acids, incorporation takes place in a linear fashion for several hours and is accompanied by a parallel increase in the optical density of the nucleic acid fraction. The further addition of guanine, uracil, cytosine, and thymine approximately doubles the rate of adenine incorporation but is without effect in the absence of amino acids. The presence of ribose has little stimulatory action. Table 10 shows the relative importance of the various additions, and it can be seen that the more

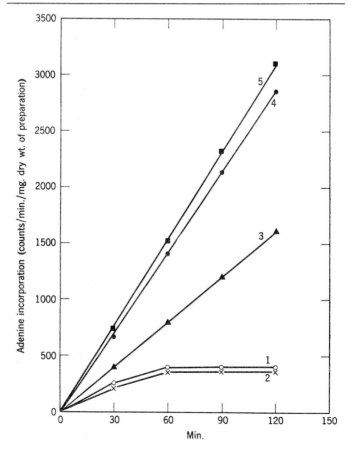

Fig. 9. Time-course for the incorporation of adenine into the nucleic acid fraction of disrupted staphylococcal cells. Incubation mixture contains ATP and hexosediphosphate in all cases, in addition to radio-active adenine and additions as follows: 1, no additions; 2, glutamic acid; 3, mixture of 18 naturally occurring amino acids; 4, as 3, plus mixture of purines and pyrimidines; 5, as 4, plus ribose. Quantities and conditions as in ref. 12.

TABLE 10

Factors Required for the Incorporation of Adenine into the Nucleic Acid Fraction of Disrupted Staphylococcal Cells

Composition of Incubation Mixture

^{14}C-Adenine, 1.7 μmoles	+	+	+	+	+	+	+
Guanine, 100 μg	+	+	+	−	+	+	+
Uracil, thymine, 100 μg.	+	+	+	+	−	+	+
Ribose, 100 μg.	+	+	+	+	+	−	+
Amino acid mixture, 18 amino acids, 400 μg. each	+	+	+	+	+	+	−
Ribonucleic acid, 1.0 mg.	−	+	−	−	−	−	−
Incorporation factor, 1 unit	−	−	+	+	+	+	+
Adenine incorporation: counts/min./mg. dry weight of disrupted cell preparation	172	4340	5734	2451	4819	5426	400

Incubation mixture contains ATP, hexose diphosphate, and buffered salts solution to 3.0 ml. in all cases; cells depleted of nucleic acid before incubation; details as in ref. 12.

important components of the incubation mixture (other than the incorporation factor) are guanine and the amino acid mixture. If an incomplete amino acid mixture is added, there is again an increase in radioactivity of the nucleic acid fraction during the first 30–60 min. of incubation; the size of the increase varies with the nature and number of the amino acids in the mixture, but continued linear incorporation takes place only with the complete mixture. If the nucleic acid fraction, after adenine incorporation under optimal conditions, is separated into DNA and RNA, it is found that approximately 88% of the radioactivity resides in the RNA fraction.

If the disrupted cell preparation is depleted of nucleic acid prior to incubation, it is found that there is then very little incorporation of adenine even in the presence of the complete mixture of amino acids, purines, pyrimidines, ribose, and ATP. The incorporation may amount to less

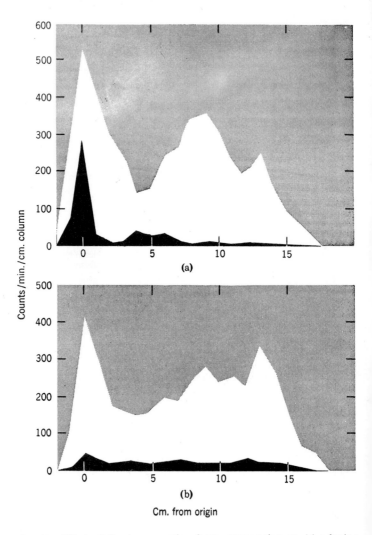

Fig. 10. Effect of the incorporation factor preparation on (a) adenine and (b) uracil incorporation by disrupted staphylococcal cells incubated under conditions optimal for nucleic acid synthesis. Nucleoprotein extracts subjected to electrophoresis in starch. Black portions = incorporation in nucleic acid-depleted cell preparation; white portions = increased incorporation in presence of incorporation factor. General conditions as in refs. 12 (this chapter) and 5 (Chapter 2).

than 2% of that obtained in non-depleted preparations. Addition of the extracted nucleic acid to the incubation mixture restores the ability to incorporate adenine. This loss and restoration of adenine incorporation is very similar to that which occurs with respect to amino acid incorporation, where restoration can be obtained equally well by adding incorporation factor preparation to the medium. Table 10 shows that incorporation factor similarly restores adenine incorporation to the same extent as an excess of nucleic acid; corresponding results are obtained for the incorporation of guanine or uracil. The action of incorporation factor is shown very effectively in Fig. 10 where the distribution of radioactivity in nucleic acid fractions obtained by electrophoresis of extracts of disrupted cells is given for preparations incubated with labelled adenine or uracil in the presence and absence of the incorporation factor under conditions optimal for nucleic acid synthesis. It is clear that the factor preparation is an essential requirement for RNA synthesis.

In the course of the experiments on adenine incorporation it was sometimes observed that the incorporation factor preparation was less effective than nucleic acid in promoting adenine incorporation, particularly when chloramphenicol was present in the incubation medium, as shown in Table 11. The nucleic acid preparation used in these experiments was the whole nucleic acid extract from the staphylococcus, and consequently it contained both RNA and DNA. This discrepancy between nucleic acid and incorporation factor in the presence of chloramphenicol was observed in experiments in which the depletion of nucleic acid had been highly efficient so that incorporation was reduced to 2–3% of that in the undepleted control. It was shown above that the proportion of the incorporated ade-

TABLE 11

Effect of Chloramphenicol on Adenine Incorporation in Presence of Incorporation Factor

Composition of Incubation Medium					Adenine Incorporation, counts/min./mg.	
ATP	Amino Acid Mixture	Purines, Pyrim- idines	Nucleic Acid	Incorpor- ation Factor	Chloram- phenicol Absent	Chloram- phenicol Present
+	+	+	—	—	50	83
+	+	+	+	—	1576	3564
+	+	+	—	+	1631	1582
ATP	Amino Acid Mixture	Purines, Pyrim- idines	Whole Nucleic Acid	Incorpor- ation Factor	DNA	
+	+	+	—	—	—	112
+	+	+	+	—		2681
+	+	+	—	+	—	861
+	+	+	—	+	+	2617
+	+	+	—	—	+	481

nine residing in the DNA fraction in experiments with un-depleted cells was about 12%; when nucleic acid is removed from the cell preparation and incorporation promoted by the incorporation factor, the proportion of the incorporated radioactivity in the DNA fraction falls to less than 6%. The addition of chloramphenicol reduces this again to less than 3%. Consequently, in cells which have been efficiently depleted of nucleic acid so that residual DNA is very small, there is little or no synthesis of DNA during incubation with purines, pyrimidines, amino acids, ATP, and incor-poration factor. Under these conditions the synthesis of RNA is also restricted. However, if small amounts of DNA are added to the incubation mixture containing incor-poration factor, then full restoration of adenine incorpora-tion is obtained. From these results it appears that synthesis of RNA in the staphylococcus requires the presence of amino acids, ATP, purines, pyrimidines, the incorporation factor preparation, and DNA.

Deoxyribonucleic Acid Synthesis. A cell-free extract of *Escherichia coli* contains a polymerase capable of the synthesis of polydeoxyribonucleotides from mixtures of the deoxynucleoside triphosphates of the four bases found in DNA.[13-15] The reaction requires the presence of DNA to act as primer and can be represented as

$$
\begin{matrix}
n\,\text{dAP-P-P} \\
n\,\text{dGP-P-P} \\
n\,\text{dCP-P-P} \\
n\,\text{TP-P-P}
\end{matrix}
+ \text{DNA} \rightleftharpoons \text{DNA—}
\begin{bmatrix}
\text{dAP} \\
\text{dGP} \\
\text{dCP} \\
\text{TP}
\end{bmatrix}_n
+ 4(n)\text{P-P}
$$

where dA, dG, dC, and T represent the deoxynucleosides of adenine, guanine, cytosine, and thymine respectively, P-P-P = triphosphate, and P-P = diphosphate. The polymerase differs from the somewhat similar polynucleotide phosphorylase in that it requires the presence of the four triphosphates for optimal activity, the amount of polymer formed with one triphosphate being less than 2% of that formed with the four mixed substrates. When one triphosphate is used as substrate, the reaction involves the addition of the corresponding nucleotide as a new end group to the DNA primer, and it may be that polymerisation by the enzyme always proceeds by the addition of nucleotide residues to the end of an existing polynucleotide. The question of specific nucleotide sequences, or the imparting of information, to the polymer is so far unanswered, although replication of the DNA used as primer may occur under certain circumstances.

Whether DNA synthesis *in vivo* is dependent on amino

acids is less clear than in the case of RNA synthesis. The presence of amino acids certainly influences DNA synthesis,[3, 5, 9] but synthesis is not abolished in amino acid-requiring mutants incubated in the absence of the specific requirement.[5, 16]

Chloramphenicol and Nucleic Acid Synthesis

In the presence of growth-inhibitory concentrations of chloramphenicol, protein synthesis is inhibited whereas RNA synthesis continues and may be enhanced.[8] Gros and Gros [9] have shown that this synthesis requires the presence of all the essential amino acids but is limited in that synthesis stops when the RNA content of the cells is approximately doubled. Neidhardt and Gros [17] found that the RNA formed by *Escherichia coli* under these conditions is unusual in that it is unstable and breaks down with the liberation of nucleosides and phosphate if incubation is continued after removal of the chloramphenicol. Addition of the antibiotic stopped the course of the breakdown and resulted in a resynthesis of RNA which appeared to be amino acid-independent. Horowitz, Lombard, and Chargaff [18] have confirmed the instability of the RNA formed in the presence of the antibiotic and shown that there is rapid breakdown of this RNA even in the presence of chloramphenicol but that this is then compensated by a more rapid rate of synthesis. Consequently the presence of the antibiotic leads to a rapid turnover of RNA, whereas such turnover is negligible in the cell during normal growth.

In view of the discovery that at least two types of ribonucleic acid—soluble *rna* and macromolecular RNA—are concerned in protein synthesis, it is desirable to know the nature of the ribonucleic acid affected by the presence of chloramphenicol. Pardee, Paigen, and Prestidge [19] investigated the electrophoretic distribution on starch of nucleoprotein extracts of *E. coli* and found that the normal cell gave rise to two components moving toward the anode. The minor, faster component was of smaller molecular weight than, and different base composition from, the major slow-moving component. If nucleic acid synthesis had occurred in the presence of chloramphenicol, the newly synthesised material was located in the faster-moving component; consequently the new material was either of smaller molecular weight than normal or was more readily dissociated during preparation. The chloramphenicol-treated material was readily dissociated from protein, whereas the major component in the normal cell extracts was tightly bound to protein. Ultracentrifuge patterns of extracts from normal and chloramphenicol-treated cells showed that the 29 S component prominent in the normal picture was missing or greatly decreased in the antibiotic-treated material. This finding has been confirmed by Dagley and Sykes,[20] who have observed that the diminution of the 29 S component is accompanied by a marked increase in peaks at 18 and 14 S.

Figure 11 shows that similar changes can be observed in the distribution of adenine-labelled nucleic acid extracts from the disrupted staphylococcal preparation when chloramphenicol is added to the incubation medium. The antibiotic suppresses incorporation of adenine into the slow-moving components (although the suppression is not complete) and increases incorporation into the fast-moving fractions. Figure 11 also shows the distribution that is obtained when adenine incorporation takes place in the presence of an incomplete amino acid mixture; it appears that omission of essential amino acids has an effect similar to the addition of chloramphenicol.

These results can now be correlated with those described in Chapter 2 for the action of chloramphenicol on amino

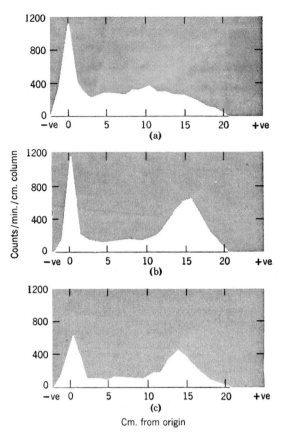

Fig. 11. Effect of incubation conditions on electrophoretic distribution of adenine incorporation by disrupted staphylococci. (a) Distribution of radioactivity along starch column after electrophoresis for 4 hr. at 20 v./cm. in tris buffer pH 7.6 of nucleoprotein extracts obtained from disrupted staphylococci after incubation with labelled adenine for 2 hr. under conditions optimal for nucleic acid synthesis (incubation mixture contained ATP, hexosediphosphate, mixture of 18 amino acids, guanine, uracil, thymine, and ribose); (b) as for (a) with the addition of 30 μg. chloramphenicol/ml. during the incubation; (c) as for (a) except that the amino acid mixture used during incubation was incomplete and lacked lysine, alanine, glycine, and glutamic acid.

acid incorporation. Figure 4 shows that the antibiotic has little or no effect on the binding of glutamic acid by fast-moving electrophoretic fractions but suppresses incorporation into the slow-moving components; in the same way Fig. 11 shows the similar results obtained for adenine incorporation. In the presence of chloramphenicol, both glutamic acid and adenine are incorporated into the fast-moving components, and the binding of glutamic acid by these components is alkali labile, reversible, and refers to material not precipitated by hot trichloroacetic acid. Gros [21] has reported that chloramphenicol does not affect the incorporation of amino acids by the soluble *rna* fraction of *E. coli* although it may retard the rate of fixation and release of the amino acyl residue. When these findings are taken in conjunction with those, discussed above, on the molecular size of the RNA synthesised in the presence of the antibiotic and on the instability and turn-over of this material, it becomes evident that chloramphenicol inhibits the later stages of the polymerisation of oligonucleotides to nucleic acid and leads to accumulation of intermediates which are able to react reversibly with amino acids. The properties of the amino acyl-nucleic acid complexes formed in the presence of chloramphenicol are similar to those of the amino acyl-*rna* which has been described as an intermediate carrier in protein synthesis. This raises the question of the relation of the chloramphenicol-*rna* to "soluble *rna*" and the relation of the latter to the macromolecular RNA of the protein-forming ribonucleoprotein. If the soluble *rna* of liver cells is labelled with both adenine and an amino acid, there is evidence that both labels are transferred to the microsome during the final stages of incorporation,[22] so that the soluble *rna* complex may become polymerised to form ribonucleoprotein. On the other hand, present knowledge of the size of the amino acid acceptor in soluble *rna* would suggest that such an explanation is less probable than that the *rna* molecule acts simply as a carrier of an amino acyl residue or possibly an amino acyl-nucleotide residue; this situation will be clearer when more definite information is available concerning the true nature of the acceptor structure in the soluble *rna*. Pardee *et al.*[19] suggest that their incorporation studies do not support the idea that the small molecular weight components of *E. coli* extracts are precursors of macromolecular RNA, and base composition studies show that the chloramphenicol-ribonucleic acid is different from, and more heterogeneous than, the normal *rna*. All the evidence is compatible with the theory that the first stages in protein synthesis involve the formation of an amino acyl-polynucleotide complex and that chloramphenicol inhibits the latter stages of polymerisation or transfer of the complex.

The inhibition of growth produced by sublethal concentrations of chloramphenicol is partially released by phenylalanine,[23] tyrosine, tryptophan, glycine, and indole,[24-27] so it has been suggested that the antibiotic can be regarded as an amino acid analogue (with particular reference to phenylalanine[23]). It is possible that chloramphenicol may react with a soluble *rna* component and so displace or prevent the incorporation of an amino acid; this would effectively prevent any final polymerisation dependent upon the coming together of 20 specific amino acyl-*rna* structures in a predetermined manner and might well result in the turn-over and instability described for the "ribonucleic acid" produced in the presence of the antibiotic. A similar result would follow if the chloramphenicol molecule displaced or became part of the acceptor with the consequent formation of an abnormal amino acyl intermediate.

There is also the problem of the selective nature of

chloramphenicol toxicity. The absence of reports of definite and striking results with chloramphenicol in mammalian tissues suggests that there must be differences in the mechanisms of protein synthesis between bacterial and other tissues. Studies of the activities of membranes and ribonucleoprotein particles seem to be pointing to differences in the cytological organisation of the mechanisms, and it may be that chloramphenicol is pointing to differences in the nature, composition, or organisation of intermediate stages in the protein-synthesising mechanism.

The Action of the Incorporation Factor on Nucleic Acid Synthesis and Amino Acid Incorporation

The incorporation of amino acids depends upon the presence of ribonucleic acids, but it would appear from the work described in Chapter 2 that nucleic acid can be removed from the disrupted staphylococcal cell and replaced, as far as the result on amino acid incorporation is concerned, with the incorporation factor preparation. It is now apparent that the factor preparation promotes the synthesis of RNA so that, under condition 2, the promotion of amino acid incorporation is accompanied by promotion of RNA or polyribonucleotide synthesis. Figure 12 shows the effect of the presence of incorporation factor on the incorporation of adenine and glutamic acid in parallel samples from the same batch of nucleic acid-depleted disrupted cells; it can be seen that enhanced incorporation of glutamic acid into any fraction is accompanied by equally enhanced incorporation of adenine incorporation in that fraction. Clearly the incorporation factor cannot be said to have *replaced* nucleic acid, but its action on amino acid incorporation can be attributed to its action in promoting the formation of nucleic acid (or polyribonucleotides) and so providing amino acyl acceptors.

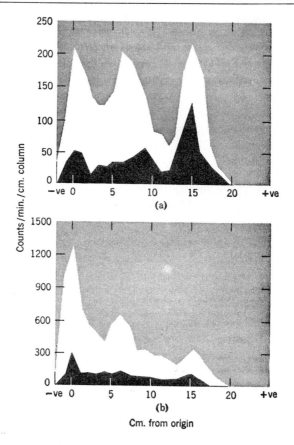

Fig. 12. Effect of incorporation factor upon the incorporation of (a) glutamic acid and (b) adenine when disrupted staphylococci are incubated under condition 2 and the nucleoprotein extracts then subjected to electrophoresis (ref. 5, Chapter 2). Black portions = incorporation in nucleic acid-depleted staphylococcal cells; white portions = stimulation of incorporation by presence of incorporation factor.

The effect of the incorporation factor on glutamic acid incorporation under condition 1 is not so readily explained on this basis. As shown in Fig. 9, there is little labelling of the nucleic acid fraction when incubation takes place with ATP and glutamic acid only. Zone electrophoresis shows that this labelling occurs throughout the range of nucleic acid fractions and is not confined to the fast-moving fractions. The labelling that takes place under condition 1 is reduced in the nucleic acid-depleted preparation and is promoted by the presence of incorporation factor; the promotion does not apply to the fast-moving components any more than to the others. It is possible that a degree of turn-over or reorganisation of existing nucleic acid takes place during condition 1 incubation, and that the effect of incorporation factor in promoting glutamic acid incorporation is again related to an underlying provision of acceptors.

The incorporation factor(s) thus appear to be essential for the synthesis of ribonucleic acid or, possibly, for the formation of amino acyl precursors of both protein and nucleic acid. It may be that the factors are coenzymes of enzyme systems involved in these processes, but, as yet, few such enzymes have been identified. One possibility would be the "activating enzyme" system which is believed to give rise to an amino acyl-adenyl monophosphate as product, but it has already been shown in Chapter 2 that the incorporation factor preparation has no activity in the amino acid-dependent pyrophosphate exchange reaction. A second possibility would be the polynucleotide phosphorylase described by Grunberg-Manago, Ortiz, and Ochoa.[10] The reaction

$$n\,\text{ADP} \rightleftharpoons (\text{AMP})_n + \text{P}$$

where ADP = adenosine diphosphate, P = orthophosphate, and $(AMP)_n$ = polyadenylate, is carried out by the disrupted staphylococcal cell and can be measured by incorporation of label into ADP when incubation takes place in the presence of ^{32}P-phosphate. The activity is depressed by nucleic acid depletion of the cell preparation, but no significant stimulation by the incorporation factor preparation has been obtained; the depression of activity during depletion may be due to removal of polyribonucleotide primers.

Actions of the Incorporation Factor Preparation in Other Systems. Weiss, Acs, and Lipmann [28] have shown that the incorporation of amino acids by pigeon pancreas fractions is dependent on the presence of a soluble polynucleotide. Dr. Weiss has kindly tested the action of incorporation factor in this system and has found that it is unable to replace the polynucleotide component.

Reuss [28a] has studied the action of the factor preparation on the growth in culture of chicken fibroblasts and finds that 0.01 unit/ml. doubles the rate of mitosis (1 unit of factor is equivalent in the disrupted staphylococcal preparation to that amount having the same effect on glycine incorporation as excess nucleic acid). Wagle, Mehta, and Johnson [29] have described a B_{12}-dependent incorporation of amino acids in microsomal preparations from B_{12}-deficient rat livers, and Wagle (private communication) finds a marked stimulation of incorporation by the factor in the absence of added B_{12}.

On the Possible Nature of Incorporation Factors

The methods so far used for the preparation of the incorporation factor(s) have yielded amounts too small for any direct chemical characterisation to be undertaken. In the absence of such direct information, other approaches must be sought.

Properties of the Incorporation Factor Preparations.
Studies have been made on two preparations (described in
Chapter 2): the "glycine incorporation factor" and the more
recent preparation with wider activities.[30, 31] Most of our
information has been obtained with the latter preparation
and the properties set out below relate to this preparation;
in certain details the earlier "glycine incorporation factor"
appeared to differ in properties and in such cases the differences are set out in parentheses.

1. In the nucleic acid-depleted, disrupted staphylococcal
cell the incorporation factor preparation promotes the incorporation of glycine, aspartic acid, glutamic acid, leucine,
phenylalanine, lysine, arginine, adenine, guanine, and uracil
to the same extent as excess nucleic acid. (The "glycine incorporation factor" promoted the incorporation of these
amino acids but only in the cases of glycine and aspartic
acid was the factor as effective as nucleic acid.)

2. The activity of the preparation is unaffected by heating to 100° for 60 min. in N NaOH.

3. The activity of the preparation is destroyed by heating
to 100° for 60 min. in N HCl. (The glycine incorporation
factor was unaffected by such treatment but was destroyed
by heating for 3–4 hr. in N HCl.)

4. The preparation obtained by acid hydrolysis as in (3)
inhibits glycine incorporation.

5. On electrophoresis on paper at pH 10.5 in carbonate
buffer, the active material moves 5–10 cm. toward the cath-
ode in 4 hr. at 20 v./cm. No movement takes place on
electrophoresis in borate at pH 9.0, phosphate at pH 6.0
or 2.0, acetate at pH 5.0, or formate at pH 3.5.

6. On paper chromatography, the active material moves
with $R_F = 0.8$ with isopropanol/ammonia as solvent, and
with $R_F = 0.7$ with ether/ethanol/ammonia as solvent.

7. A solution of the incorporation factor containing 20 units/ml. has no significant specific absorption in the ultra-violet at 260 mμ.

8. The preparation is not inactivated by treatment with sodium periodate.

9. Aqueous solutions of the factor are colourless; dried preparations have the appearance of a colourless gum.

Activities of Known Substances. A wide variety of substances has been tested for activity during the last three years, but none has so far been found which fulfills all the above requirements. In view of the possibility that vitamin B_{12} may be concerned in protein synthesis,[29] we have paid particular attention to this substance and possible derivatives. Slight activity, insignificant in comparison with that of the incorporation factor preparation, has occasionally but inconsistently obtained with B_{12} and pseudo-B_{12} at $10^{-5}M$ concentration; preparations of B_{12}-peptide and B_{12}-coenzyme (kindly provided by Dr. Hedblom and Dr. Barker respectively) have had no greater activity. The incorporation factor preparation has been assayed for B_{12} activity by *Euglena* growth tests which have given completely negative results (Woods, private communication).

During the early stages of the work on the separation of the factor, it was noted that the incorporation of glycine could be promoted by high concentrations (0.1–1.0 mM) of uridine and guanosine.[32] These nucleosides were clearly not the incorporation factors themselves, as even crude preparations of the factors were active at much smaller concentrations as judged by the optical density at 260 mμ, and it seemed that the activities of the nucleosides were probably due to contamination with factor-like substances. We have returned to this point recently and have found

that many ribosides possess activity at this concentration of
0.1–1.0 mM. Activity has been found in the following, in
decreasing order of efficiency: kinetin riboside, inosine,
guanosine, uridine, adenosine, 6-dimethylaminopurine riboside, and thymine riboside. Cytidine is almost devoid of
activity. The corresponding bases, deoxyribosides or ribo-
tides, and ribose itself have little or no significant activity.
Quantitatively the activities vary in a curious manner; the
ribosides retain the same relative order of activity, but the
activity of the more effective members such as inosine may
equal that of the incorporation factor in one batch of disrupted cells but have only 30–50% of the activity of incorporation factor in another batch a few days later. The
reason for this variation has not been discovered; it suggests that the ribosides undergo metabolism to more active
substances and that batches of cells differ in their ability
to carry out this metabolism. Webster [33, 34] noted that amino
acid incorporation by pea seedling particles could be increased by the presence of ribosides at concentrations of
1 mM, but only the "natural" ribosides including cytidine
were active in that system. The stabilities of the incorporation factor preparation would be in accord with those of a
purine riboside (those of the glycine incorporation factor
resembling those of a pyrimidine riboside).

The ribosides tested in these experiments are of a high
degree of purity, but there remains the possibility that their
activity lies in contaminants. This has been investigated in
two ways:

(a) The electrophoretic and chromatographic behaviour
of inosine is very different from that of the incorporation
factor (see Table 12). Consequently a preparation of inosine has been subjected to ionophoresis at pH 10.5 in carbonate buffer and also developed on paper in isopropanol/

TABLE 12

Electrophoretic and Chromatographic Properties of Ribosides

| | Electrophoresis at pH 10.5 and 20 v./cm. | | Chromatography | |
| | Movement in 3 hr. | | | |
	to Cathode, cm.	to Anode, cm.	Isopropanol/ ammonia, R_F	Ether/ ethanol/ ammonia, R_F
Guanosine	..	12	0.18	
Adenosine	3	..	0.4	
Inosine	..	18	0.2	0.2
Uridine	..	15	0.38	
Cytidine	4	..	0.32	
Kinetin ribo- side	6	..	0.75	0.8
Incorporation factor	6	..	0.8	0.7

ammonia; in each case, the paper has been cut and eluted at the position where inosine was located and also where the incorporation factor activity would be found. Activity has run quantitatively with inosine.

(b) A number of uridine derivatives has been made available, through the courtesy of Dr. A. L. Morrison of Roche Products Ltd., so that the activity of this substance could be investigated in detail. Uridine was purified through the following stages: uridine → 2′:3′-O-isopro-pylidene uridine → 2′:3′-O-isopropylidene-5′-O-toluenesul-phonyl uridine → 2′:3′-O-isopropylidene-O²-5′-cyclouridine → uridine; the final product had significantly the same activity as the initial material and three other uridine preparations. 2':3'-O-Isopropylidene uridine is inactive but becomes active on removal of the isopropylidene group. Cytidine is without significant activity but becomes active on treatment at $100°$ for 1 hr. in N NaOH, the appearance of activity coinciding with the formation of uridine by deamination. It would seem reasonable to deduce that the activity lies in uridine itself. Commercial uridine preparations are now known to contain 5'-ribosyl uracil as an impurity; [35, 36] we are indebted to Dr. W. Cohn for a sample of this substance which proved to have activity similar to and slightly less than that of uridine itself. Uracil, uridine phosphate, uridine diphosphate, O^2:2'-cyclouridine and ribose are inactive. 5'-Acetyl uridine has an activity approximately 10% of that of uridine.

In all cases optimal activity of the ribosides is displayed at concentrations approaching $10^{-3}M$ and activity is insignificant at $10^{-5}M$. At low concentration the activities of the ribosides are additive, but no significant increase of activity has been obtained with mixtures of ribosides and B_{12} or pseudo-B_{12}. With the exception of kinetin riboside, the ionophoretic and chromatographic properties of the ribosides are very different from those of the incorporation factor preparation; the properties of kinetin riboside agree closely with those of the incorporation factor, but 20 units (in terms of activity)/ml. would correspond to an optical density at 260 mμ of the order of 100 compared with negligible values for the factor preparation. The absence of electrophoretic mobility in borate and of inactivation by periodate (properties 5 and 8 on pp. 91 and 92) indicate that the factor cannot in any case be a simple riboside.

If these results have any meaning in connection with the incorporation factor problem, they would appear to suggest that the factor is some form of active riboside. In this connection it is interesting to recall that the action of ribonuclease on amino acyl-polyribonucleate is to release amino acyl-adenosine.[37]   If ribonuclease has this action *in vivo,* it may be that the "soluble *rna*" should be regarded as a source of riboside derivatives and that the factor plays its rôle somewhere in the interchanges that go on at this level.

Inhibitors of Incorporation

It might be possible to obtain some light on the nature of the incorporation factor(s) by studies of the nature of substances which will inhibit incorporation.   The reactions mediated by the factor preparation (amino acid and purine or pyrimidine incorporation) are themselves complex ones measured by an over-all response which may depend on the functioning of many different components.   Nevertheless it is possible to determine certain criteria which must be obeyed by an inhibitor before it can be considered an antagonist of the factor or an inhibitor of factor-mediated reactions.   Incorporation depends on energy supply and transfer and amino acid "activation"; these processes can be studied in isolation and are known not to depend on the factor, so we can eliminate inhibitors which are found to act upon these systems.   Incorporation of an amino acid such as glycine relates to processes culminating in protein and in cell wall syntheses, and incorporation factor mediates both series of processes.   Experience suggests that, if an inhibitor is without effect on one of the series, then the inhibition obtained will be partial and will display a plateau value (see Chapter 1).   Consequently an inhibitor related to the incorporation factor will, in sufficient concentration, reduce glycine incorporation to nothing.   Likewise, the incorporation factor mediates the incorporation of both amino acids and purines so that any inhibitor affecting only one of these is unlikely to act on a factor-dependent reaction.   With these considerations in mind,

we have surveyed a number of inhibitors and antimetabo-
lites for their ability to inhibit the incorporation of glycine
and adenine by the disrupted staphylococcal preparation.[38]
Three main groups of inhibitors have been found.

1. Substituted Benzimidazoles. Tamm [39-42] has investigated the relationship between structure and activity in the
benzimidazoles as inhibitors of virus growth. He found
that inhibitory activity increased with the degree of halo-
gen substitution in positions 4, 5, and 6 while the most
potent inhibitors were obtained by the further substitution
of β-ribofuranoside groups in position 1. These benzimidazole derivatives are also active as inhibitors of glycine or
adenine incorporation, but their relative activities differ
from those found in the virus system. Inhibitory activity
increases with substitution of either CH_3— or Cl— in positions 4, 5, and 6, but the further substitution of either
α- or β-ribofuranoside in position 1 abolishes inhibitory
action; 5:6-dimethyl-1-β-D-ribofuranosylbenzimidazole has
some inhibitory action at $10^{-3}M$ but is stimulatory at
lower concentrations, so that it resembles the other ribosides discussed above. Tamm's results are consistent with
the hypothesis that benzimidazole derivatives inhibit virus
growth by competing with purine ribosides. In the light
of the action of ribosides (shown in the previous section)
on amino acid incorporation, it would seem that such a
competition could also form the basis of inhibition of incorporation but that the mechanism affected is not the
same in both systems. The inhibition of glycine incorporation is antagonised by 6-amino-4-hydroxybenzimidazole.

2. Diaminodichlorbenzene Derivatives. 1,2-Dichloro-4,5-
diaminobenzene proved to have the same inhibitory action
as 5,6-dichlorobenzimidazole and indicated that substituted
benzenes should be investigated along the lines followed
by Woolley and Pringle,[43] who suggested that such sub-

stances inhibit the synthesis of riboflavin and B_{12} from their precursor, dimethyldiaminobenzene. Substitution of —OH and NO_2 in positions 1, 2, 4, and 5 gave potent inhibitors of incorporation while 1:2-dichloro-4-(p-nitrobenzenesulphonylamido)-5-nitrobenzene (DCDNS) was the most effective inhibitor of this series both in our own incorporation studies and in the investigations of Woolley[44] and his collaborators.

3. 8-Hydroxyquinoline and Derivatives. Although chelating agents such as ethylenediaminetetraacetic acid and α:α-dipyridyl were without significant action on glycine or adenine incorporation, 8-hydroxyquinoline (oxine) was even more inhibitory than DCDNS. Oxine was highly inhibitory at $M \times 10^{-5}$, but less effective at higher concentrations. A similar type of concentration effect has been observed by Albert, Gibson, and Rubbo[45] in studies of growth inhibition by oxine; they suggested that oxine acts by forming chelate complexes with metal ions and that the 1:1 oxine/metal complex is the inhibitory agent whereas the 2:1 oxine/metal complex, formed when the oxine is present in excess, is non-toxic. Oxine has relatively little effect on glycine incorporation by nucleic acid-depleted staphylococcal cells but, at $M \times 10^{-5}$ concentration, abolishes the stimulation of incorporation brought about by the incorporation factor preparation (see Fig. 13).

The results shown in Fig. 13 suggest that the site of oxine action is the activation of incorporation by incorporation factor. The incorporation factor preparation passes without loss of activity through Dowex 50 in the Na^+ form, so that it would appear that metals do not form an essential part of the preparation although it may be that combination of the factor with its site of action requires the presence of metal ions and can be blocked by metal-oxine complexes. The inhibition produced by oxine is antagonised by 6-amino-4-hydroxybenzimidazole, which also antagonises

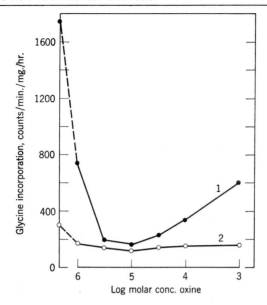

Fig. 13. Effect of 8-hydroxyquinoline on glycine incorporation by nucleic acid-depleted disrupted staphylococci in presence (curve 1) and absence (curve 2) of incorporation factor.

the action of benzimidazole derivatives and the inhibition produced by the products of acid hydrolysis of the factor preparation (see p. 91).

Inhibitor studies have not given any clear guide to the nature of the incorporation factor but have provided some interesting facts to be interpreted when the chemistry of the factor has been elucidated.

The Nature of Protein Synthesis
or Schemes of Things To Come

It would be unnatural to finish a discussion of this sort without the presentation of a scheme, and Fig. 14 provides

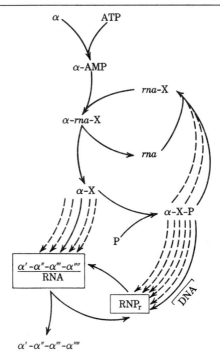

Fig. 14. Protein synthesis (1959). α = amino acid, ATP = adenosine triphosphate, rna = soluble ribonucleic acid; AMP = adenosine monophosphate, DNA = deoxyribonucleic acid, P = purine/pyrimidine, RNA = ribonucleic acid, RNP_r = ribonucleoprotein $\alpha'\text{-}\alpha''\text{-}\alpha'''\text{-}\alpha''''$ = peptide chain.

a diagram descriptive of possible pathways of protein synthesis in the light of knowledge in 1959. Neither the scheme nor its details have been established on any firm basis, but the diagram represents the general outline on which we plan tomorrow's experiments.

Two types of reaction are involved: the "individual"

type concerned with a single amino acid (or nucleotide), and the "integrating" type concerned with the coming-together of a large number of amino acyl and/or nucleotide residues to produce a specific polypeptide, polynucleotide, or nucleoprotein. Our experiments to date seem to have greater success with the first than with the second type of reaction.

Amino acid "activation," portrayed as a reaction with ATP, and the fixation of the activated residue by soluble *rna,* are "individual" reactions. Although no proof is yet forthcoming, it seems probable that the next stage in amino acid incorporation is the release of an amino acyl complex shown as $(\alpha\text{-}X)$ in the diagram. X may be a polynucleotide, a riboside, an as yet undetected substance, or even an incorporation factor. The close relationship between nucleic acid and protein syntheses could arise through the existence of a common type of precursor such as $(\alpha\text{-}X\text{-}P)$.

The integrating reactions give rise to proteins, ribonucleic acids, and ribonucleoproteins and occur only when all the necessary precursors $(\alpha\text{-}X$ or $\alpha\text{-}X\text{-}P)$ are available. Present theories seem to envisage two forms of integration reaction: the formation of proteins by integration of amino acyl residues $(\alpha\text{-}X)$ on a preformed RNA template, and the formation of ribonucleoproteins by integration of amino acyl-nucleotide structures $(\alpha\text{-}X\text{-}P)$. The information theory requires us to postulate mediation of the second integration by DNA. A less specific form of polymerisation may lead to the formation of "soluble *rna*" from $(\alpha\text{-}X\text{-}P)$ mixtures in which certain members are missing or unbalanced.

It would appear that omission or abnormality of any of the 20 or more $(\alpha\text{-}X)$ or $(\alpha\text{-}X\text{-}P)$ structures would prevent the formation of specific proteins or ribonucleoproteins but would not necessarily prevent the production of incomplete *rna* complexes which would be characterised by small molecular weight, heterogeneity, ability to combine reversibly with amino acids, and, probably, instability. The presence of chloramphenicol produces essentially these results, and it may be that its action can be attributed to interference with the formation of (α-X) as discussed on p. 86.

It can be seen that this scheme, like all good schemes, hinges on the properties of an unknown substance X.

En Voie

I began these lectures with a reference to the approach of those of us who seek to instruct others in the science and art of microbiology. I have recently glanced back through some of the notes that I used for my lectures fifteen years ago and, going into the even dimmer past, at notes I took during my own period of instruction as a biochemist and microbiologist. A tremendous change of attitude is apparent through the years. Fifteen to twenty years ago we were concerned with mechanisms of breakdown: breakdown of amino acids, of sugars, of nucleotides, and of fats. True, we talked of "energy production" and the need of a living organism for energy to make large molecules from small, but we paid scant attention to mechanisms of such building processes—unless we suggested that they took place by reversal of the breakdown reactions we listed with such care. "Biosynthesis" was a beautiful concept, about as precise as the need of "protoplasm" for "bios." Today, my course of lectures at Cambridge is happily entitled "Biosynthesis in micro-organisms" and I complain that there is time only for a mere skeleton of present knowledge—while all that stuff about deaminases and decarboxylases must be squeezed into the more elementary courses.

And there is another change taking place at the present time. As biochemists throughout the world have laboured on intermediary metabolism and its enzymes, they have produced more and more mechanisms which appear to be the same in Man and Microbe. This has produced a tacit belief that "fundamental" biochemistry is the same for all living creatures, and the obvious differences between such creatures represent specialisations that protect, buffer, and maintain the fundamental biochemistry against the vicissitudes arising in the course of evolution. It follows that an enzyme, say glutamic decarboxylase, or a process, say protein synthesis, might as well be studied in a bacterium, a plant, or a liver cell. But the function of the enzyme as a component of a brain cell may be very different from the function of the similar enzyme in a bacterial cell,[46] and we shall not understand the biochemistry—in the true and complete sense of the term—of that enzyme without reference to its cellular context. The biological organisation of a process is as important as the chemical nature of that process. In mammalian and plant cells, this organisation can be seen in the existence of mitochondria, membranes, and microsomes, and, in spite of the technical problems involved, we recognise that we must study these both as biochemical units alone and as integral parts of the whole cell. The electron microscope shows us that the internal organisation of the bacterial cell is simpler in the sense that there is less obvious differentiation of organelles. This seems to be reflected in a different morphological distribution of some of the components involved in protein synthesis, and we are faced with the possibility, discussed before, that the intricacies of specific protein syntheses may depend upon the detailed structure of the cell. And so our biochemical thought moves from consideration of the chemical reactions that yield structural components to contemplation of the idea that structural components organise or mould the chemical reactions. Meditation over an electron micrograph of a bacterial cell wall or the endoplasmic reticulum of a liver cell brings conviction that the position of synthesis within the cell must be as important as the chemical synthesis itself.

For this reason these lectures have been entitled "Synthesis and Organisation in the Bacterial Cell." It is only too obvious that there is far more to do than has so far been accomplished. The title should also include "disorganisation," as most of the results discussed in these pages have been concerned with the consequences of disorganisation—frequently on so drastic a scale that it is a miracle that anything of significance survives. Dr. Marjory Stephenson, to whose guidance and stimulation I owe so much, wrote [47] "We are in much the same position as an observer trying to gain an idea of the life of a household by a careful scrutiny of the persons and material arriving at or leaving the house; we keep accurate record of the foods and commodities left at the door and patiently examine the contents of the dustbin . . ." Things have advanced since that time (1929); now we bomb our way into the house and study the dying spasms of the remains.

To extend the simile in a more hopeful fashion: some of us have found our way into a laboratory and are plunging about in the dark. We have upset some of the solutions; we have broken some of the apparatus and are trying to put it together again in the dark; some of us have started disintegrators under the impression that they are adding machines; we are getting in each other's way, but someone, someday, will press the lamp switch and then we shall see the purpose of it all.

REFERENCES

1. Gale, E. F., and Folkes, J. P., *Biochem. J., 53,* 483 (1953).
2. Borek, E., Ryan, A., and Rickenbach, J., *J. Bacteriol.,* **69,** 460 (1955).
3. Gros, F., and Gros, F., *Biochim. et Biophys. Acta,* **22,** 200 (1956).
4. Ycas, M., and Brawerman, G., *Arch. Biochem. Biophys.,* **68,** 118 (1957).
5. Pardee, A. B., and Prestidge, L. S., *J. Bacteriol.,* **71,** 677 (1956).
6. Michelson, A. M., *Nature,* **181,** 375 (1958).
7. Hecht, L. I., Zamecnik, P. C., Stephenson, M. L., and Scott, J. F., *J. Biol. Chem.,* **233,** 954 (1958).
8. Gale, E. F., and Folkes, J. P., *Biochem. J., 53,* 493 (1953).
9. Gros, F., and Gros, F., *Exptl. Cell Research,* **14,** 104 (1958).
10. Grunberg-Manago, M., Ortiz, P. J., and Ochoa, S., *Biochim. et Biophys. Acta,* **20,** 269 (1956).
11. Spiegelman, S., *Recent Progress in Microbiology,* Almqvist & Wiksell, Stockholm, 1959, p. 81.
12. Gale, E. F., and Folkes, J. P., *Biochem. J.,* **69,** 620 (1958).
13. Lehman, I. R., Bessman, M. J., Simms, E. S., and Kornberg, A., *J. Biol. Chem.,* **233,** 163 (1958).
14. Bessman, M. J., Lehman, I. R., Simms, E. S., and Kornberg, A., *J. Biol. Chem.,* **233,** 171 (1958).
15. Adler, J., Lehman, I. R., Bessman, M. J., Simms, E. S., and Kornberg, A., *Proc. Natl. Acad. Sci. U.S.,* **44,** 641 (1958).
16. Kerridge, D., *J. Gen. Microbiol.,* **21,** 168 (1959).
17. Neidhardt, F. C., and Gros, F., *Biochim. et Biophys. Acta,* **25,** 213 (1957).
18. Horowitz, J., Lombard, A., and Chargaff, E., *J. Biol. Chem.,* **233,** 1517 (1958).
19. Pardee, A. B., Paigen, K., and Prestidge, L. S., *Biochim. et Biophys. Acta,* **23,** 162 (1957).
20. Dagley, S., and Sykes, J., *Nature,* **183,** 1608 (1959).
21. Lacks, S., and Gros, F., *J. Molecular Biol.* (in press).
22. Hoagland, M. B., *4th Intern. Congr. Biochem., 1958, Symposium on Proteins,* Vol. VIII, Pergamon Press, London, p. 199.
23. Woolley, D. W., *J. Biol. Chem.,* **185,** 293 (1950).

24. Mentzer, C., Meunier, P., and Molho-Lacroix, L., *Compt. rend.,* **230,** 241 (1950).

25. Truhaut, R., Lambin, S., and Boyer, M., *Bull. soc. chim. biol.,* **33,** 387 (1951).

26. Molho, D., and Molho-Lacroix, L., *Bull. soc. chim. biol.,* **34,** 99 (1952).

27. Bergman, E. D., and Sicher, S., *Nature,* **170,** 931 (1952).

28. Weiss, S. B., Acs, G., and Lipmann, F., *Proc. Natl. Acad. Sci. U.S.,* **44,** 189 (1958).

28a. Reuss, S., private communication; to be published.

29. Wagle, S. R., Mehta, R., and Johnson, B. C., *J. Biol. Chem.,* **230,** 137 (1958).

30. Gale, E. F., *Harvey Lectures,* **51,** 25 (1957).

31. Gale, E. F., and Folkes, J. P., *Biochem. J.,* **69,** 611 (1959).

32. Gale, E. F., *Proc. Intern. Congr. Biochem., 3rd Congr., Brussels, 1956* (ed. Liebecq, C.), 345.

33. Webster, G. C., and Johnson, M. P., *J. Biol. Chem.,* **217,** 641 (1955).

34. Webster, G. C., in *The Chemical Basis of Heredity* (eds. McElroy, W. D., and Glass, B.), Johns Hopkins Press, Baltimore, 1958, p. 268.

35. Kemp, J. W., and Allen, F. W., *Biochim. et Biophys. Acta,* **28,** 51 (1958).

36. Cohn, W. E., *4th Intern. Congr. Biochem., 1958, Abstr.,* 29.

37. Zachau, H. G., Acs, G., and Lipmann, F., *Proc. Natl. Acad. Sci. U.S.,* **44,** 885 (1958).

38. Gale, E. F., and Folkes, J. P., *Biochem. J.,* **67,** 507 (1957).

39. Tamm, I., *Science,* **120,** 847 (1954).

40. Tamm, I., *Bull. N.Y. Acad. Med.,* **31,** 537 (1955).

41. Tamm, I., *J. Bacteriol.,* **72,** 43 (1956).

42. Tamm, I., *Symposium Soc. Gen. Microbiol.,* **8,** 178 (1958).

43. Woolley, D. W., and Pringle, A., *J. Biol. Chem.,* **194,** 729 (1952).

44. Woolley, D. W., *J. Am. Chem. Soc.,* **74,** 5450 (1952).

45. Albert, A., Gibson, M. I., and Rubbo, S. D., *Brit. J. Exptl. Pathol.* **34,** 119 (1953).

46. Gale, E. F., and Epps, H. M. R., *Biochem. J.,* **36,** 600 (1942).

47. Stephenson, M., *Bacterial Metabolism,* Longmans, Green & Co., London, 1929, Introduction to the First Edition.

INDEX